MY SECRETS

JOAN COLLINS

BOXTREE

For my beautiful daughters
Tara and Katy
And my delightful god-daughters
Victoria, Rachel, Chloe,
Milica, Coco and Cara

Paperback edition first published in Great Britain in 1995 by Boxtree Limited, Broadwall House, 21 Broadwall, London SE1 9PL

Original hardback first published in Great Britain in 1994 by Boxtree Limited

1 3 5 7 9 10 8 6 4 2

ISBN: 0 7522 1625 2

Designed by Hammond Hammond
Typeset by SX Composing Ltd, Rayleigh, Essex
Printed and bound in Great Britain by Butler and Tanner, Frome, Somerset

A CIP catalogue entry for this book is available from the British Library

ADVICE TO THE READER

Before following any medical, dietary or exercise advice contained in this book, it is recommended that you consult your doctor if you suffer from any health problems or special conditions or are in any doubt.

CONTENTS

Prologue · 7

· CHAPTER ONE ·
LEARNING TO LOVE YOURSELF · 13

· CHAPTER TWO ·
POSITIVE THINKING · 31

· CHAPTER THREE ·
NOTHING SUCCEEDS LIKE HARD WORK · 41

· CHAPTER FOUR ·
LESS STRESS · 51

· CHAPTER FIVE ·
THE BEST WAYS TO AGE · 59

· CHAPTER SIX ·
YOU ARE WHAT YOU EAT · 71

· CHAPTER SEVEN ·
SUPPLEMENTARY BENEFITS · 76

· CHAPTER EIGHT ·
FIT FOR LIFE · 81

· CHAPTER NINE ·
SKIN DEEP · 97

· CHAPTER TEN ·
THE MAGIC OF MAKE-UP · 123

· CHAPTER ELEVEN ·
CLASSIC CLOTHES SENSE · 133

· CHAPTER TWELVE ·
WOMEN & LOVE · 151

· CHAPTER THIRTEEN ·
THE A-Z OF ALL THINGS GOOD & BAD · 159

ACKNOWLEDGEMENTS & PICTURE CREDITS · 191

PROLOGUE

NOW THAT WE are well into the 1990s, the time has come to look clearly at the beauty philosophies of the past. In the nineties our credo should be a positive and *balanced* way of life, because no amount of cosmetics, grooming or exercising will make you look good on the *outside* if you don't feel good inside.

The quest for the elusive elixir for youth has been going on since the dawn of civilisation. Our ancestors employed an extraordinary variety of magic spells, herbs, medicines and food to revitalise themselves and retard their ageing process. But alas no magic potions have ever existed, nor will they. It is only through common sense, proper exercise and nutrition, and most *important* of all a positive attitude towards getting older, that a woman can reach her potential of being lovely throughout the seven ages of woman, and I'm going to tell you how to begin.

I wrote a book about beauty fourteen years ago, and since then much has changed in terms of what we can do to improve ourselves and our lives, mentally, physically and emotionally.

In the 1990s we must stop being fitness freaks, health fiends, diet junkies and cosmetic queens, and relax into a simpler way of life, exploring, discovering and appreciating what is *inside* us, what makes us tick, and using that to make things happen for us.

I believe that true lasting beauty *does* come from within and that good health, vitality and energy all spring from the same vital, vibrant source: you; and that you get the face and body you deserve. According to folklore getting older means a gradual loss of looks, but today this doesn't have to happen, though any woman whose happiness depends *just* on her youthful looks will be disappointed.

Today you can look how you choose because ideals have changed; what is considered beautiful today is much broader and more diverse than in the past. Old or young, you should no longer allow yourself to

be judged by some outmoded criteria of the 'right' way to look or behave.

The way one is brought up has lasting significance in terms of the attitudes we develop as adults. My own parents were a huge part of what has made me the woman I am today. They gave me a tremendous sense of values, a sense of what is right and wrong, a respect for authority, for older people and people of different cultures, and a belief in hard work. In no way did they spoil or over-indulge me. My father went out to work and brought home the bacon, my mother stayed at home and looked after the house and children. Daddy was a stern disciplinarian, hard and remote in many ways, but with a great sense of humour and love of life. Mummy was beautiful, glamorous (but not glitzy), adored dressing up and going out, but at heart she was a homebody whose world revolved around her family, the archetypal wife and mother. She adored her life and was totally fulfilled.

Dressed to the nines! With my Aunt Pauline, who used to borrow me on the occasional weekend, for a stroll around Brighton.

If you were born in the 1930s or 1940s, and grew up in the 1950s and 1960s you were solidly indoctrinated to believe that by thirty-five you would be over the hill, finished, kaput. In our gym slips, the bloom of youth still on our cheeks, we were often told that for *all* women past thirty-five, it was goodbye to productive, romantic, sexual, fulfilling *life*!! After thirty-five you were a non-event, a dried-up old husk. Her child-bearing years over, a woman could contemplate a boring future of knitting patterns, cocoa by the fire with purring cat on lap, and the advent of grandchildren, to whom she would dispense her worldly wisdom.

That attitude has, thank goodness, changed radically, in Western society at least, in the past few decades. Women have finally grabbed a toe-hold on the slippery bank of equality. 'Only a toe-hold?' you say, 'We're there aren't we? We've been there for years, surely?' In some ways we may have been there for years but we still have a long way to go. I believe that too many women still don't know how to reach their full potential and I hope this book will pave the way for new recruits.

Blocks are still put in our way by society, men, parents, children and colleagues, and they stop us reaching our full potential and real goals. Often a woman thinks it's not feminine to feel or act a certain way; that she's not being a 'real woman' if she isn't always ready with a

MY SECRETS

shoulder to cry on or providing endless time for everyone who demands her love and nurturing.

Bolstering other people's feelings of security and well-being is considered more important than meeting her own needs, and any woman who rebels against that concept is seen as selfish. So it's up to *us* to take the bull by the horns, stand up straight and have our voice heard. We are NOT a *minority*, we are an *equality* – but today's feminism has nothing to do with the militant women's libbers of the 1960s. To be a 'real woman' you don't have to become a pale imitation of a man. You don't have to scrub off your make-up, and chuck out your bra and mini-skirt.

Why should wearing eyeliner make you a 'bimbo'? Take pride in being womanly, and having a woman's attributes. Looking good is the prerogative of *every* woman if she cares enough to make the effort, and doesn't feel *guilty* about doing it. And *don't* listen to those who say you're frivolous and trivial if you care about your appearance. It's insulting to women to equate beauty and pride in their femininity with lack of brainpower.

The 1990s are more confusing than ever for women. The pressure on us has intensified. We are supposed to be equal to men, but too many of us aren't treated equally at all, and because women are still considered by many men to be second-class citizens, we all too often have an inbuilt 'I'm not really any good' complex.

The only thing we can be sure of today is that too often we are supposed to be *all* things to all people: good wife, wonderful mother, successful career woman, terrific cook, and great in bed. Who can do that? No one, not even Superwoman.

So many women are torn between career and home, guilty if we abandon our children, unfulfilled if we don't work. The average mother must function as chauffeur, housekeeper, cook, shopper, psychiatrist and teacher. And, in order to succeed, a career woman must be much better at her job than a man in the same position. Then, if she does succeed, she often finds herself despised and ridiculed because there still persists that age-old image of the female as the weaker sex.

In order to survive and thrive in this male-dominated world, women must take charge of themselves and their own lives. In order to do that, we must look after ourselves, both physically and emotionally.

M Y S E C R E T S

We must make sure that we are in peak condition. A stressed-out, unhappy, unhealthy woman can't help herself, let alone anyone else.

We don't spend nearly enough time looking after ourselves.

This book is going to tell you exactly *how* to take care of yourselves; how to nurture your creativity, your self-respect, your inner and outer health and your well-being. I believe that beauty, if it is nurtured and maintained, can last way beyond the thirties, and well into the sixties, seventies and eighties.

Because life is about appreciating what you are *now* instead of what you *were*, there are no hard and fast rules for being beautiful at all ages – only guidelines, most of which are common sense, but I have many ideas and suggestions that have worked for me, that I am going to share with you: how to become more successful, more confident and more positive; how to be alone but not lonely; and how negativity can wreck your life.

These are the lessons I have learned, the wisdom, experience and knowledge of both my inner and outer self.

I have now reached a stage where I am content with my life. I feel I have achieved in my career, I have good friends and a wonderful man in my life, my children are thriving, and now I want to pass on some of the knowledge I've gained to other women who can perhaps learn something from what I have learned.

With my beloved children, Tara, Katy and Sacha, who bring me enormous joy. Christmas 1987.

So this book is not just about outer beauty, but about the *whole* woman – the inner woman, her aspirations and the environment she wants to create for herself and those around her. Some of my discoveries, I hope, can be yours.

MY SECRETS

CHAPTER ONE

Learning to Love Yourself

SELF-ESTEEM AND INDEPENDENCE

EARLY YEARS

A S A CHILD I had no self-esteem. I didn't even think I was particularly pretty. When I was a tiny tot I sat in the hairdresser's chair having my fringe cut and was amazed to hear the hairdresser exclaim, 'My, doesn't she have beautiful eyes.' I looked at my eyes in astonishment. They didn't seem to be any different from anybody else's; but at that moment, as I became aware that my eyes were perhaps a little more unusual than others, a sense of self-esteem started to develop.

I still had a low opinion of the way I looked when I went to RADA, having just turned sixteen. I was one of the youngest students there, and totally awestruck by the beauty and poise of some of the older students. I remember one ravishing 'older woman' (she must have been all of twenty-two) who had the kind of face I had always wanted. She had long, gypsy-like black hair, white skin, green eyes and full red lips. She wore the student uniform of the day: a black turtle-neck, gold earrings, a multitude of bracelets, a long full skirt and black ballet slippers. I quickly tried to emulate this paradigm of sophistication, who, I noticed, was always the epicentre of any group, either in the canteen or in the coffee bar where we lingered after classes.

In this girl's presence I felt like some small brown mouse, so I was amazed to notice that many of the older boys often stared at me too. My hair was long with a fringe like my idol's, but it was not black, just

Caught in the net! A little shrimp about to be captured by her father. Bognor Regis, aged 4.

MY SECRETS

boring darkish brown. My eyes were not bright green, they were a sort of muddy grass colour. My skin, thanks to sunbathing to which I was addicted, was not white, but somewhat sallow, with spots. I considered myself too fat, too short, too gawky, and all in all a bit of a wreck.

I hung out with my two best friends, Eilleen Moore and Susan Stephen. Eilleen had a beautiful face, Susan had an exuberant personality, and I, in spite of the fact I thought I was overweight, had a good body. As a trio we were nicknamed Face, Figure, and Personality. Even though I was Figure, I had such a lack of self-esteem that I really could not understand why.

Shortly after this, I started modelling for teenage magazines and, much to my surprise, when a scout saw a photograph of me in *Spotlight*, (the theatrical casting bible that my father had kindly put me in) I was cast in a Swedish television commercial.

Fetchingly attired in a tightly-boned, turquoise bathing suit, I knelt before the camera and dipped into a big box of Smarties. Take after take after take we shot, and ever greedy for sweets, I devoured handful after handful. Even when we weren't shooting I carried on gorging myself, so that by lunchtime I felt thoroughly sick. As I lay weakly on a sofa in my dressing-room, gasping for air and sipping water, I felt someone patting my hand and I opened my bloodshot eyes to see the director sitting beside me. 'You must learn to control yourself, Joan,' he said. 'You are a beautiful girl but you obviously have *no* self-control.' True enough, I thought to myself. He gave my knee a paternal squeeze and said, 'Self-control is the true sign of a person who will succeed. You have the potential for success. I saw you in a play at RADA and you were quite good, but I can see that you could easily destroy your looks with your gluttony.' I gulped, tears filling my eyes. 'Sorry,' I whispered. 'I won't do it again.' He patted my hand again. 'When we do the long shots this afternoon you can fake eating the Smarties. After all, you are an actress aren't you?' I nodded numbly. 'Now remember what I said,' he added. 'Self-discipline is the *first* step on the ladder of self-esteem and success, and self-confidence which comes from self-esteem is the *single* most important personality trait that you need to succeed in business, or to be a successful leader in any venture.'

He shot me an avuncular, Swedish smile, and feeling encouraged I smiled weakly back. We finished the shoot and later, when I was alone,

Learning to love myself and the camera. And beginning a life-long love affair with the sun.

MY SECRETS

I thought long and hard about his words. That was some of the best advice I ever received and I've never forgotten it.

RESPECT YOURSELF

Many people have asked me since then how one can develop self-esteem. The answer, I believe, is that it can *only* come from within yourself. It comes from being proud of your own achievements, however much they might be mocked or belittled by others. It comes from *knowing* that you are doing the *right* thing. Don't listen to other people's opinion of you. No matter if they seem cleverer than you. *You* must believe in *yourself*.

Some children are brought up by parents who constantly tell them how beautiful, brilliant and fabulous they are, and give them every possible advantage in life. But those children don't always grow up with self-esteem. Other children are brought up with brutal or insensitive parents, with lack of care and consideration, and with no family stability, and yet *still* acquire self-esteem and success. Why? The answer I think lies in the sad fact that many of us use the enormous power of our minds to create a *negative* reality rather than a *positive* one.

My beautiful mother, Elsa with brother Bill, and me aged 13 pretending to have the self-esteem I hadn't yet discovered.

So many of us think of ourselves as actually unworthy. When someone pays us a compliment, a voice inside us sneers, 'He's lying – I'm not pretty or clever or funny at all.' Then, when we have our hearts set on something, that inner voice echoes: 'You don't deserve it.' And when someone criticises us, that voice agrees: 'Oh yes, you are useless/stupid/ugly.' We must all learn not to be adversely affected by criticism. Criticism can wound bitterly and deeply, particularly from a loved one, but criticism, like sarcasm, is the easiest form of negative attack. It's much too easy to criticise anyone, anything and everything.

MY SECRETS

If you ask most people to make a list of their goals they would probably only be able to put down one or two things. To be happy. To have plenty of money. But most of them wouldn't really have a life plan. That's because they don't take their lives seriously enough to create one. Lack of self-esteem comes from thinking that *one is just not good enough*, which can undermine all positive things in your life. Low self-esteem breeds apathy – the inability to act or feel, which appears to be almost endemic in society today.

. . .

It can be difficult, if you are in a situation where you are being put down and undermined, to feel good about yourself. So *do not ever let criticism affect the part of you that respects you*; remember, that there is no such thing as the way you *should* be. Just be *who* and *what* you are, to the best of your ability.

Once you feel good about you, which has a great deal to do with asserting and respecting yourself, you will find it much easier to cope with negative outside influences.

If you feel dowdy, no-good, downtrodden, unsuccessful, fat, slothful, or just plain disagreeable, it's too easy for these negative feelings to become reinforced by the slightest everyday mishap. All it takes is somebody cutting in front of your car in traffic, pushing you in the supermarket queue, cursing if you get in their way in the street, to make you feel unworthy.

There are far too many women who are abused by their husbands, boyfriends, or fathers. I wonder how many of these women could, given the choice, stop their cruel treatment? Do they fear asserting themselves so much that they can't say, 'No, don't do that. I don't like it. Stop it!'

Often there is a pattern in some women who *allow* themselves to be hurt both physically and emotionally; it's a numbing pattern of lack of self-esteem, and self-worth, and lack of believing and listening to that inner voice which says, 'I'm okay. I'm all right. I'm a good person, a nice person. I'm a person who really counts.'

This pattern usually comes from early childhood, bad school experience, or bad parenting. It's a tragic fact that

The three faces of an up-and-coming actress.
Opposite: In my first play *The Praying Mantis* on tour in England.
Below: The image that the Rank Organization liked me to portray.
Bottom: Rome 1954. My first American film, *Land of the Pharoahs,* and beginning to take hold of my life and career.

MY SECRETS

so much misery is caused to children by their parents, without them even realising it.

But if you know it, if you can see where much of your lack of self-esteem originated, that is the FIRST step to regaining it. Search inside yourself and try to remember its beginnings. You must start feeling positive, and only by becoming positive, more self-aware, more proactive, more interested in the world around you, can you find self-esteem.

Don't hold yourself back, either at work or social gatherings, by letting your feelings of inferiority get the better of you. Try to feel good about yourself, even if you are intimidated. If you allow this intimidation to overcome you, you will feel (and therefore act) shy, stupid and awkward. If you start feeling like this – stop it at once. You are just as good as other people. Maybe better.

You may feel jaded, sluggish, exhausted, bored by life. Perhaps you feel empty, drained, unmotivated, and wonder 'Who cares about me? Who really gives a damn? Why should I bother to improve myself or my life, to try to get a better job, to diet or exercise more? What's the point?' If you think you are slipping into any of these sluggish ruts, it's time to start taking control of your life. Grab hold of the steering wheel and get moving!

THIS IS YOUR LIFE

For many women the empty-nest syndrome is one of the most shattering blows of their life. The day my eldest child, Tara, first went to nursery school at three was one of mine. My heart sank as I watched her tiny figure disappearing behind the school gates. A brave hand gave a cheery wave and I gulped back a tear. Luckily her baby brother Sacha was still at home so when he tottered off to nursery school a couple of years later I had already realised that I did *not* want to experience this horrible sense of loss from not having my children with me all day.

I had semi-retired from acting and it had semi-retired from me, so I decided to do something that interested me – something new and stimulating. I started doing some interior decoration and design in friends' houses. I called the new company TARALEX Interiors, after the Christian names of my two children. After studying the subject avidly, I developed a flair for it and soon became moderately successful.

MY SECRETS

Most importantly it gave me something to occupy my mind while the children were at school.

I started to realise then how *essential* it was to add another string to your bow apart from being mother, wife and home-maker. I began to understand how a woman *must* become her own 'Master of the Universe'.

Think of your life as a play or a movie. *You* are the writer, the director and most of all the star, and the people around you are the supporting players. You can and you must make things happen. If you can practise this process of visualisation on a daily basis it will eventually become second nature.

I am by no means advocating total selfishness – lying in bed all day gobbling chocolates, reading romance novels and completely neglecting your kids and husband. But too many women never put themselves first; they always put their own needs and feelings on the back burner.

Respect breeds respect. It's quite true that those who have the most self-respect, strength and self-reliance are usually the leaders of their group. Whether they are a film director or the queen bee of the knitting circle, those who believe in and trust themselves and their own opinions make others believe in and trust them too.

Self-esteem is saying, 'I want to do what I want to do, and not always what *you* want to do' to your parents, your partner and friends, or your children. Why pretend to be a football fanatic if you would prefer to go to a matinée, or the ballet? Why cook hamburgers for the family every night when you would rather have quiche? So many women go along with doing what they *don't* want to do, to please those closest to them, thinking they will lose their love if they don't, feeling that it's wrong to indulge themselves. But it isn't. If *you* can't spoil yourself, pamper yourself, make yourself feel good, then who will? You owe it to yourself to be number one in your life. And that doesn't mean that you are becoming a selfish bitch, which many people will try and make you feel. Smile sweetly and say, 'Yes I am, aren't I?' Don't let insults or derogatory remarks affect *your* opinion of yourself.

Loving *yourself* is the first step to being able to love other people, and letting yourself do what *you* want to do (within reason) is the most important thing that you can do to start building your self-esteem.

*T*o *love oneself is the beginning of a lifelong romance.*

(OSCAR WILDE)

MY SECRETS

LIFE BEGINS AT FORTY

Life is *not* all down hill over forty, believe me. I know so many women who say they feel better than ever at this age. It is ridiculous to accept that a woman cannot and should not reach even greater heights in her life, and in her career, when she has passed the age when men in the street turn to stare at her.

However, the unfortunate statistics are that there are far more available and fabulous over-forty women than there are available and fabulous over-forty men. There are certainly many attractive men around, but when you investigate you'll find that many of them are married, already involved, or gay. So it is important for a woman over forty, divorced, widowed or single, who has a career, whose children have grown, and who is by herself, to rely on her *own* network of friends. You don't have to be rich to have friends; you don't have to be young, beautiful or even desperately amusing. All you have to be is *yourself*: warm, caring, interested and open to new people and ideas.

If you open yourself up to the world of art, of books, of music, of dancing, of museums, or go to some of the many new clubs and groups now available for women, you will find that you need not be lonely for long. There are many people out there in the same boat as you – women who don't have a mate or partner, or whose children have left the nest. Many of these women have developed a positive approach to life. They began by doing what I recommend in this book. They take a long hard look at themselves and see what they can do to improve themselves – physically and mentally.

I have a friend in her fifties, whose husband recently died. She had spent her life being a caring mother to her five children, and what is known as 'a good wife'. She also had a flourishing career as an interior decorator. After her husband died she grieved for nearly two years, then gradually began seeing other men. She was getting on with her own life. Her children, however, all in their late twenties and thirties, were aghast.

'How can you *do* this to us?' they wailed, as they drove around in their cars bought with *her* money, and decorated their nice little flats bought by her. 'You're deserting us.' These children were desperately trying to make their mother feel guilty for enjoying her new life. *Her life*. Luckily my friend did not listen to her children. She explained to them kindly but firmly that she was in a new period of her life, that she loved her children, but that they had their own lives to live and she was now going to live hers. She is now very happy living with someone in a stable relationship.

Her children have reluctantly accepted the situation, and she has remained strong enough *not* to let them dictate to her. If she had, she might have felt guilty about dating in her fifties, and given it up so as not to embarrass her children and grandchildren. She had the courage to put aside her family's opinion and convention and go calmly ahead to her next chapter, confident and assured. That woman is a winner and I would like to see more like her.

TAKING CONTROL

If your circumstances do not allow you to be totally independent, you can still achieve a certain amount of independence, even if it is for just one or two hours a day. Whether that independence is reading novels, going skating, or taking an hour off at the gym, it is *vital* that a woman regularly does something to please herself.

Too many women have been made to feel selfish if they are independent. Becoming independent is one of the most rewarding things a woman can do. Imagine knowing that *you* are in control, that you can make your own money, that you and you alone have the say in how that money is spent, knowing that when you wake up in the morning on a weekend, you can do what you want, go where you want, see who you want, buy what you want and *no-one* is going to tell you otherwise. This is something that few women can achieve until they attain the independence that a career, however humble, can provide. Nobody knows more than I, having journeyed down the aisle four times, how important men are in our lives. But I still believe that a man is not a *necessary* adjunct to a woman. Many women nowadays are able to lead profitable, healthy and fulfilled lives without having another half. I am not advocating going without men – oh no, that would not be much fun – but in 1994 it is not necessary to make a man the centre of your life. The centre of your life should be *you*, and if you love, care and respect yourself you will have much more to give, both to your man, your family, friends and children.

Unfortunately it has been indoctrinated in women for far too

That which does not kill us makes us stronger.

(NIETZSCHE)

many centuries that 'A gal ain't complete unless she's got a guy'. There is a wonderful song that Lena Horne sang, called *An Occasional Man*. The attitude was then revolutionary that a woman could be happy, free and having a hell of a time without a man around. Some people were quite shocked by these lyrics:

> '*I've got an island in the Pacific, and everything
>   about it is terrific;
> I've got papayas, peaches, sandy beaches, and,
>   an occasional man!*'

What a fabulous idea, and with all those papayas and peaches you'll never get fat!

So why is there *still* a stigma in being an unattached woman, particularly one over forty? I still remember my 'old ' maiden aunts, and great-aunts (there were a great many of them) being looked on pityingly by the rest of the family as being a bit lacking as they played the part of the modest maiden.

Unfortunately other women actively distrust attractive widows, divorcees, or spinsters, whereas a single eligible man over forty is a huge asset at a dinner party. A woman of the same status is *not*.

A single woman is made to feel her life isn't complete. Whether a single man is toothless, bald, fat or a crude drunk, he is *still* more socially acceptable than a single female.

In the 1990s, women should be able to walk into a theatre, a restaurant, anywhere alone and feel confident. We have choice now. Not only the choice to have a child or not, but the choice to have a man around or not. As long as you are confident enough not to feel over the hill, washed up, or 'past your sell-by date', being alone over forty can be enormous fun and very rewarding.

However I do know many really attractive, thirty, forty and fifty-year-old women who can't find a man they really like. So they get on with their lives. They don't wait around for him because – face it, girls – even if men are like buses and come along regularly, it may not be the number you want to catch. Why settle for any Tom, Dick or Harry? – which is what some women, so desperate for a man that they will take what they can get, often do?

If you don't have a man in your life for all seasons and all times, and many do not, we too often settle for second best just to have a man

Opposite: It's not all downhill over 40 – or even 50. Taking a break between scenes on the *Dynasty* mini-series.

around. We put up with smelly socks on the floor, dirty shirts chucked in a corner, seat up on the loo, and feet up on the table as he glugs beer and watches snooker.

'Is that all there is?' sang Peggy Lee mournfully. No it is not. Men are not the necessity to the modern woman which they were in our grandmothers' day, so it's just better not to have one unless he is the right one.

I'm not saying that men are not necessary in family life, for I am old-fashioned enough to believe that a child needs both a mother and a father, but neither a young girl starting out in life, nor a woman whose family are grown who is perhaps widowed or without a man, should feel insecure and bereft because she is manless.

Being with women can be just as much fun as men, if not more so. I've often had more enjoyment and laughs with a group of women friends than I have with a group of men. Face it, girls, who can you relax and let your hair down with more than your own sex?

CHANGE THAT ATTITUDE

Leisure time should be *your* time too. How many times have you sat bored to tears, watching a darts match, or football on television because *he* wanted to? Assert yourself. Say that you want to watch *your* favourite programme and if he doesn't like it, give him an argument. Don't just be passively bovine.

The trouble with so many women is that we have been given subtle signals all our lives that we are second-class citizens, whose opinions and wishes are not as important as men's.

Well it's high time that attitude started to change.

There are numerous examples of successful women in politics, business, the arts, or show business: Margaret Thatcher being of course *the* prime example. Whatever you may think of her, Lady Thatcher has an indomitable spirit and is a woman of strong character, fibre and steel. This was perceived by many in politics to be a flaw in her character, as the world, and men in particular, would really prefer to see women in a subservient position.

I am not convinced that the sexual revolution and the women's movement have really changed male and female attitudes. The persistent commercialisation of women as sex objects in films and porno videos contributes to their degradation, as do designers who show models walking down catwalks with circles cut out of dresses showing bare breasts. If a designer created a suit for men with the genital area cut out there would be an uproar!

I think there's a very clear yet fine line between a woman being feminine, aware and proud of her own body, and a woman using that body, that sexuality, to get ahead. I never debased myself in any way for a role, never sold myself to a producer for a job, and there were many opportunities to do so. I've had too much pride and have consequently managed to hold on to my self-esteem. I believe that women should stand up for themselves, refuse to be exploited and refuse to exploit their own sexuality. We should take pride in our femininity and our feminine qualities – warmth, nurturing, tenderness and caring; we have the ability to work on an equal basis with men, and although sometimes we may get knocked along the way, we've got to learn to be resilient. Women have been abused, misused and the appendages of men for centuries, and now we finally have an opportunity to be ourselves.

But where are our role models today? I think Princess Diana is one of the best. She's a woman of our times, a woman who cares about her children, and who works extremely hard. Many people don't realise how dedicated she is, or how difficult her life can be; when the press are waiting for her to make one wrong move so that they can pounce and criticise and she has to live almost like a nun. Margaret Thatcher is a wonderful role model – a capable woman with formidable strength.

DOUBLE STANDARD

Let me give an example of the sexual double standard of male versus female. A well known, respected theatre director, interviewed recently on television, described in some detail his promiscuous homosexual lifestyle, and how he had contracted AIDS from picking up men for casual sex on London's Hampstead Heath. He admitted quite cheerfully that he had been doing this for many years, and seemed quite relaxed about it, as did the interviewer. This director has never to my knowledge been criticised for his promiscuous lifestyle.

At the opposite end of the spectrum let us take an actress who has been married more than once, has had several lovers (but only one at a

MY SECRETS

time), and has made no secret of the fact that she enjoys the company of men. This woman is chastised, criticised, ridiculed, gossiped about, reviled, and often scorned for her interest in men, not only by the media but also by the public and stand-up male comics.

It is *still* not considered acceptable for a woman to have a past, whereas it is considered perfectly acceptable for a man to have a shady one. Whether he has relationships with women, men, or multiple partners, a man is rarely criticised for his sexual habits, indeed he is often admired for them. To sum up, gay bashing is politically incorrect but female-celebrity bashing is OK and sells newspapers! Since it is not yet politically incorrect to be rude about women, anyone can say anything about us and get away with it.

Women in the public eye are not given credit when it is deserved. Recently a London evening newspaper ran a series of profiles on women in important executive jobs in television. Next to each profile of these women they chose to print a stamp-size photograph of the woman's mate. Can you imagine them doing this if it was a series of *men* who had just received these jobs?

This negative view of women is reflected at every level in society. There is little sympathy for women who juggle the demands of motherhood, wifehood and job/career. A woman's life is in many ways far more complicated than it ever was in our mothers', grandmothers' or great-grandmothers' time. The permissive society gave us equal rights and sexual freedom but I think that this has turned around and hit us in the face. How many of us have the freedom to walk along the streets at night without fear of attack? That's not paranoia, that's a fact. There is a higher incidence of rape and abuse against women now than ever before, and little is done about it. Whatever happened to chivalry? Whatever happened to respect for women? Whatever happened to women being cherished? As for sexual equality, that means if you don't sleep with the new boyfriend on the first or second date, he will find another girl who will.

Women must combat all these negative factors by becoming as inwardly and outwardly strong and invincible as possible. Answer to no-one but yourself, and listen to your inner self, that voice that speaks the *truth*!! Don't be bullied into becoming something you're not, or into doing something you don't want to do.

MY SECRETS

SMALL PLEASURES

To make your life more pleasant you must start with your environment. I believe everyone should have their own private place, their own nest, surrounded by the things that make life a little better. These can be simple and need not be expensive. Shops are full of plants, flowers, scented candles that fill the air with subtle aromas, little pillows, and all manner of attractive, inexpensive, decorative objects that can make you feel better in your environment and boost your well-being. In a bubble bath, after a slogging twelve hours' work on the set, I can lie listening to music, with a glass of wine and a scented candle nearby, and feel the worries of the world completely evaporate. Frames cost next to nothing, and to have a photograph of your loved ones near your bed gives you a feeling of tranquillity in your special environment. Little things can give you pleasure. Music, of course, is one of the greatest sources of enjoyment. Just think, one could play music all day long, every day of one's life, and never listen to the same piece twice.

   Start savouring every second of your life by appreciating the world around you *now*. Don't put off whatever it is you choose to do until later. It's getting later now, so you had better start enjoying it. Look at the positive things in your life around you. They can give you happiness if you truly appreciate them. Being alive and well, having healthy children, hearing the birds sing, and watching the clouds scud across the sky.

However long I've lived in Hollywood I never give up my delicious English afternoon tea! Hollywood 1988.

YOU CAN DO IT

I had always wanted to write a book and, although I wrote many stories and articles throughout my teens and twenties, I never managed to get even halfway through, let alone finish them. There was always too much else to do: I was working as an actress in films and plays, I was travelling, I was involved in romances, marriages and then having my children. There simply wasn't time to write. And then fifteen years ago I sat down, determined to write and finish my autobiography *Past Imperfect*.

MY SECRETS

I put my mind to it singlehandedly, and even though I had three young children, a busy film and television career, and many other distractions, I *made* the time. I got up two hours earlier every day and went into a quiet room where I could concentrate. I gave up unnecessary outings, socialising and partying. I finished the book in six months and was delighted by my achievement. In fact I was proud of myself, and my self-esteem increased with my awareness of what I was capable of. That was in 1978 and since then I've written two more non-fiction books, two novels and now this one.

There must be something that *you* have always wanted to do – I am not suggesting writing the rival to *Gone With the Wind*, but most people have some secret desire that they have never had time to fulfil. Maybe it's to start exercising, to jog, to learn how to make a soufflé, to learn how to spell properly, to take a computer course, to draw, to paint, to design. There are endless things that are interesting and entertaining to do and learn if we can just budget our time properly. Try to believe in yourself, have goals and achieve them.

Don't let other people's negativity and jealousy force you to stop doing a project you have always wanted to do, and don't be put off by your husband, best friend, mother-in-law or children moaning 'Why are you doing that? What's the *point* of learning to needlepoint, paint, make apple pies, write articles for magazines?'

At school there were several subjects I found completely captivating, as I am sure you did. For example, geography was something I wished I could experience more outside the classroom. That is why I love to travel, and visit as many different places as possible. I love to explore and try to understand something of what makes other cultures tick. I am endlessly intrigued when I see the way other people conduct their lives. Just sitting in an outdoor café, watching the world go by, in a busy main street in Buenos Aires can give me hours of pleasure.

Painting also interested me as a child, as did history, English literature, fashion design, and journalism. But I had to make a choice, and my first choice was acting. There are so many entrancing things to do in the world, and you will find yourself more stimulated, more interesting, and more pleased with yourself if you choose to have more than one string to your bow. Who says you can't?

*T*here is no such thing as great talent without great willpower.

(BALZAC)

M Y   S E C R E T S

MAKE IT HAPPEN

Throughout our lives, if we *don't* get what we want we usually have a long list of reasons why we don't get those results. We say, 'All this is a waste of energy', or perhaps we give a convincing argument as to why we can't have what we want. Think negatively like this and your life really will not improve or go anywhere.

George Bernard Shaw said, 'The true joy in life is being used for a purpose recognised by yourself as a mighty one; the being thoroughly worn out before you are thrown on the scrap heap; the being a force of nature instead of a feverish, selfish little clod of ailments and grievances complaining that the world will not devote itself to making you happy.' Face it – the world couldn't care less about your happiness. Whatever you want it is up to *you* to make it happen. And when it happens, you'll know *you* did it!

Heraclitus, a philosopher who lived about 500 BC, said, 'Nothing endures but change.' How true. Everything in life changes – the seasons, ourselves, our children, our attitudes, our aspirations. If you are in a rut, bringing about changes in your life may be difficult; it takes real courage to look honestly at your life, discover what is not working for you, and then try to change it. Whatever is happening in your life *now* is the result of what you have done, thought, and felt for years. If you want your situation to improve, you have got to change *yourself*, what you think, what you feel, what you do. Sometimes this can be terrifying, particularly for someone who is not in their so-called 'prime'. Sometimes it can be extremely hard to change: for example, for a woman who is married to a brutal, unfeeling or uncaring man. But however difficult it may be, if we want to improve our lives and love ourselves there are things that we *can* and *must* do.

We *can* alter our attitude to life. By taking a more positive and assertive approach to it, by being less afraid of what people think, and by loving *ourselves*, truly and deeply, for what we are, we can make a huge difference to our own lives.

MY SECRETS

CHAPTER TWO

Positive Thinking

SUCCESS AND TAKING CONTROL

A**S A SCHOOLGIRL** I sensed certain negative attitudes towards me from the other girls. I don't really know why; maybe I seemed too stuck-up, was too shy and retiring, or maybe it was because I went to so many different schools and was therefore always the new girl. Those whispered comments, nasty remarks in the cloakroom, childish pranks, hurt me a great deal, but I tried not to let it affect me because even at a very young age I believed in myself and was determined to make things happen.

I now have a strong and positive self-image. When I walk into a room, or work on a set, I know that people are aware of my presence. Of course some people may dislike or resent me, but that simply does not bother me any more. You *cannot* let people's negative opinion of you affect your behaviour – if you did you would be a mouse.

When my two eldest children were at nursery school I decided it was time to return to acting in movies. I was thirty-four but looked twenty-five, so I had hope. When I told my Hollywood agent what I wanted to do, she shrieked with laughter: 'Joanie, you're *far* too old to get back into the business. Stay at home and look after your babies.'

'My babies are at nursery school,' I said stiffly.

'Well, it's too late now,' grinned my agent, with a certain satisfaction. 'You're just too old and you've been out of the business too long. Face it, kiddo – you're finished.'

'Thanks,' I said, but I vowed to myself that I would not let her put me down. I also fired that agent and got another one!

MY SECRETS

ALL CHANGE

Look honestly at everything and everyone in your life and decide what and who you want to keep, and what and who you want to get rid of. Does that neighbour who is constantly bugging you add to your well-being? No? Then cut her out of your life. Pretend she doesn't exist.

Many of the people with whom we interact socially are often deeply negative towards us but we just don't have the guts to say so or to stop seeing them. It may sound harsh but the world is full of wonderful things and people, adventures and situations that we will never experience even if we live to be a thousand. Why not then try to experience the ones you really like rather than putting up with people who don't do you any good, out of habit or pity?

The *Desiderata* says, 'Avoid loud and aggressive persons, for they are vexatious to the spirit.' I have found that I continually make new friends, and have deliberately stopped seeing certain people from my past. Selfish? Probably, but why should I have to spend what I consider to be my quality time with friends if they don't make me feel good?

I recently saw Barbara Walters on American television interviewing a legendary American socialite who had just turned ninety. The interview was fascinating not only because the lady looked at least twenty-five years younger than she was, but she spoke with the spirit and attitude of a much younger woman. When asked by Barbara Walters, 'What advice would you give somebody who is hoping to live a long and productive life?,' she replied: 'I found throughout my life that as some people get older they become quite boring, therefore each year I stop seeing certain friends that have been in my life for some time. I have substituted through the last several years younger people who are more stimulating, more fun, and bring a new point of view to my life. So when I have a dinner party or attend any social function I am not surrounded just by people of my own age, but by people in their twenties, thirties, forties, fifties and sixties as well. I appreciate it may sound callous, but it is certainly the way that has worked well for me.'

Well thumbs up to her! I don't think it's callous at all. I think she shows enormous

Definitely taking control! With Linda Evans in one of our famous fight scenes from *Dynasty*. How the feathers flew, but it was great fun.

courage and self-confidence to speak out.

Try to avoid negative situations. If you hate travelling to work in an over-crowded bus, find another way of getting there. Perhaps you could take an earlier bus, or share a car with someone at your office. It isn't always easy but I do think that one should not force oneself to put up with situations that are stultifying and negative.

If you are stuck in a job that you hate, with people you dislike, try to change the job. 'It's not that easy', I can hear you say. With unemployment and the recession most people feel lucky to have a job at all. If there is no immediate possibility of changing job, why not start by changing your attitude towards your job? Try to find things in it that you like, even if the job is as menial as filing. Why not try to file so brilliantly that everyone in the office will notice your positive attitude and promote you to a more interesting job? Sour, depressed, angst-ridden people don't get on in life. Smiling, happy, forthright, optimistic, hard-working people do. But of course none of this just falls into your lap. As Thomas Edison said: 'There is no substitute for hard work.' I certainly agree with that.

Have you ever heard it said 'Amazing how lucky hard-working people are?' Ain't that the truth. Hard work is the first step to success and it never hurt anyone, while negative thinking is the first enemy. If you have been thinking negatively for years, it will be hard to change the habit immediately, but you *must* start. Just as physical strength is gained in the gym or on your bedroom floor by the constant repetition of exercises, so getting rid of negativity will occur only when you start to practise positive thinking. So if you are handed some lemons in life, which we all are, get out the sugar and make yourself some lemonade!

THINK POSITIVE

Several years ago in California I took part in a weekend seminar called the Sedona Method (Sedona being the name of a town in Arizona where the method was originated). The basic philosophy behind the Sedona Method, is that you must try to erase from your mind *all* negative and unpleasant thoughts which prevent you from getting what you want. This made a lot of sense to me as I believe that harsh and unpleasant things that impinge upon our lives and consciousness *should* be dismissed from our minds as quickly as possible, and not be allowed

I don't want to achieve immortality through my work. I want to achieve it by not dying!

(WOODY ALLEN)

M Y   S E C R E T S

to fester there. The Sedona Method 'allows' you to have what you want by releasing the negative thoughts that prevent you from getting it. For example, when driving around looking for a parking place, instead of becoming stressed out, tense, angry and frustrated, you dismiss these thoughts from your mind, and *allow* yourself to find a parking space. And do you know something? It really works. Even if you don't always find a space nearby, the act of releasing the negative stress allows the mind to function better, and you become more relaxed.

It is amazing how much more you can achieve if you get rid of frustration and anxiety in your daily life. Of course you will always have a certain amount of stress and we are all subject to it; but it's how we *cope* with it that sorts the well-adjusted person from the burnt-out one.

It was during a break on *Dynasty* that I decided to take part in the Sedona seminar. I was suffering from several stressful situations in my personal life so I went out of interest, and to see if it really worked. The friend who took me was convinced it was the panacea for all mental (and some physical) ills. I wouldn't go quite that far but it was an extremely intriguing and absorbing experience. The techniques of relieving stress by positive thinking have been enormously useful to me. And participating in group therapy and hearing other people's problems made my own seem rather insignificant.

VISUALISATION
AND THE POWER OF HUMOUR

I believe strongly in visualisation. You are what you think you are, and what you *want* to be. If you feel strong, vibrant and good-looking, that's the aura that you'll probably give off to others and how they will think of you. If you feel weak, inept, plain and insignificant you'll give off that image too. Think yourself more beautiful, healthier, younger, stronger, cleverer, more ambitious. It's amazing what the process of visualisation can do, and how rewarding it can be.

If you can't have everything you want, here's some suggestions on how to get anything you want:
1. Visualise yourself having or doing whatever it is you want.
2. Know exactly *what* it is that you want. Write it down.
3. Want it above everything else in the world.
4. Focus all your attention on what you want. Become obsessed by it.

Opposite: South of France 1988. I'm always happiest when the sun is shining and I don't have to get up at 5 o'clock in the morning for work.

MY SECRETS

5. Know you can have it. Visualise it almost as if it was already yours.
6. Do all that is required to get it.
7. Give up everything that opposes what you want.
8. Pretend that you've got it.

Visualisation is the technique of imagining something that you really want and *willing* it to happen. Strangely enough most people don't even know what they really want out of life. I'm not talking about wanting to win the pools but about more realistic goals. You must *know* what you want before you go after it.

Visualisation was demonstrated brilliantly in a book by Norman Cousins called *Anatomy of an Illness*. Diagnosed as terminally ill, Cousins was given six months to live and his chances of recovery were virtually nil. He felt that the stress, anger and depression that he had experienced all his life had contributed to his illness. He wondered if being negative can make you ill, can being positive make you better? He decided to experiment on himself. Laughter being one of the most positive activities he knew, he rented all the comedy movies he could find. He read lots of entertaining and amusing books, and he asked his friends to telephone him with any funny, witty stories or anecdotes they had heard.

Norman Cousins was in terrible pain, too much pain even to sleep properly, *but* – and this is something which I think proves that visualisation can be a source of strength – after he had laughed solidly for a few minutes, he found each time that his pain was relieved for several hours and he was then able to sleep. He recovered from his illness, and put the reason for his miraculous recovery down to visualisation.

LUST FOR LIFE

Many people as they age become more and more lethargic as they feel their vitality and energy seep away. One can certainly blame the stresses of modern life, but the actual *lack* of energy, the lack of will to do anything, the lack of a *joie de vivre*, is a recent growing phenomenon. A real lack of energy cannot be cured with tonics and pep-up pills. Energy comes from eating the right food and from a positive outlook on life and doing things.

How often have you woken up in the morning feeling utterly

MY SECRETS

exhausted from a bad night's sleep tossing and turning, or dragged yourself into the bath or shower after eight hours, forced coffee down your throat, and still felt dreadful?

The next time you feel like that, instead of that cup of coffee try some bending, stretching, sit-ups and warm-up exercises and you will find that after a few minutes your body releases endorphins which charge you with more energy. The more exercise you do the more energy you will have to do other things.

I was lucky to be born with a metabolism that gives me a very high degree of energy but I also work at it. I am focussed, and single-minded. I try not to fritter away my energy. I have specific goals in my life which I continually set. For example, right now it's to finish this book and share my secrets with you! Both my parents had a high energy level. When I was a child my mother cooked, read, knitted, visited friends, talked to and played with her children. My father worked ten or twelve hours a day, played cards with his friends and went to football matches. With the example of busy, active parents to follow I too was constantly involved in projects. We were all busy as bees most of the day, and evenings too, and we were never *ever* bored.

The only time I totally turn off is on Sundays when I just see friends and family, read tons of newspapers, watch television, and generally potter about. Sunday night is when I am usually the least energetic. Having done a great deal less that day than I usually do, my body feels lethargic, bloated, lazy! I usually make up for it on Monday morning by getting up early and being as active as I can.

How many times have you heard someone say, 'If I only had the energy'? Whenever I hear that, whether from a young or older person, I shake my head sadly and think *what a waste*. We *all* have the potential for energy and to achieve much more than we usually do. Most people have reserves of energy which they have never tapped into. How often have you heard or read a story of someone who has been in a car accident and on finding their loved one trapped beneath the car has, with superhuman effort, lifted the ten tons to save their beloved's life? Those people have miraculously tapped into their secret and inner reserves of energy that they didn't know they had, but which deep down all of us do.

Occasionally I wake up feeling full of energy but by mid-afternoon

it's disappeared. This does not happen often, and I can usually put my finger on the reasons why: not enough sleep, eating the wrong food, too much heating in the room, smoking and drinking too much, and allowing work-pressure, and stress to get the better of me.

So how can we harness our energy and have it at our fingertips whenever we want? The answer is you have to enhance your lifestyle by putting into yourself all the things that will boost your energy. For some people eating the right food, exercising, and taking extra vitamins just isn't enough. They need other energy enhancers: yoga, meditation, massage, acupuncture, aromatherapy, sometimes even psychoanalysis – all help different people to achieve more of their energy potential.

One of the most energy debilitating things in modern life is the hidden pollution that is in every particle of air that we breathe every second. Many people I know have recently started to develop all kinds of strange new allergic reactions and illnesses. I know far more intelligent, hard-working and reasonably healthy people now who have hay fever than I did ten years ago. Far more with asthma, food allergies and strange coughs and flu-type viruses that no amount of medicines and antibiotics can cure. I believe that our immune systems are having to work extra hard these days to fight the chemicals and the poisons that are in the very air we breathe, the water we drink, the foods we eat, and rid them from our systems. Unfortunately, unless we go and live on some totally unpolluted island, it isn't going to be possible to live a pollution-free life, so we *must* boost our immune system by eating a healthy diet to give us the maximum energy, vitality and protection.

One of the most important ways to create energy is by sleep. I don't mean ten hours of soggy, hung-over snoring: if we do that on the occasional Saturday night we usually wake up on Sunday morning feeling horrible. I mean the pure, unbroken, sometimes dreamless sleep, which we can only achieve if our minds are free from anxiety and stress.

I don't believe it's necessary to sleep eight or nine hours. Sleep is like sex – some people need more of it than others. Find out how much sleep you actually *need*, and then stick to the amount that suits you. When Lady Thatcher was Prime Minister she only needed four hours a night to function properly. When I was doing *Dynasty* I was going on all cylinders on five or six hours' sleep. Nowadays I need seven. It all depends on your metabolism, the time of year, and your stress level.

MY SECRETS

The noise in cities from buses, cars, those hideously loud motorcycles, construction work, not to mention the sound of jumbo jets flying over the roof-tops creates an enormous amount of stress and can also interfere with our sleep. So many of us live in cities where our neighbours often have their radios and televisions on full volume and give raucous parties; lorries rattle down the streets all night, and planes take off and land at all hours. There is little we can do about noise other than try to shut it out, and there are many good ear-plugs on the market. I use them on plane trips to Los Angeles and they really do block out most of the engine sound. Another thing to help you sleep is an eye mask. You can buy these at any chemist.

All too often we put our energy into needless things. Do you really *need* to spend two hours baking a birthday cake for your mother-in-law, when you could go to a health food shop or a good bakery and find an excellent one ready made? Do you really *need* to do the family laundry every day? Couldn't you save it up, put it all in a big bag and do it once a week? It's important to try and save your energy for the things that are important to *you*, and that you really enjoy. And when you really enjoy things, you'll be more energetic than ever. Never forget, energy begets energy.

Waiting for the next bus to come along! With apologies to Steven Berkoff. *Decadence* 1993.

Another way of wasting an enormous amount of energy is being stuck in a relationship which doesn't make you happy, but not having the guts to get out. Often a woman will stay with a man she doesn't really care for because of the fear of not finding another one. I have already said men are like buses – if you wait long enough another one will come along. So if you're saddled with one that isn't up to par, why not get rid of him, and take on a better model?

Staying in a stressful relationship that doesn't make you happy does nothing but drain your energy. I don't mean the kind of saccharine happiness portrayed in romantic paperbacks or technicolored 1940s movies. That kind of happiness isn't realistic in today's society. But as long as you are reasonably content in your relationship you can work on creating the energy you need to devote yourself to other things in your life. More than anything I think that attitude has *everything* to do with our lives, how we age, how we look, how we feel, and how we want to be. If you've got the right attitude you are on the right track. And that goes for *everything* from eating properly, to thinking positively.

MY SECRETS

CHAPTER THREE

Nothing Succeeds Like Hard Work

I CAN'T THINK of one person I know who has achieved success by luck alone; it's always by hard work. My father was fairly strict and he set high standards for all his children, but at the same time he allowed me to have my head. When I said I wanted to be an actress, he told me in no uncertain terms that if I was not good enough to pass the entrance exam to RADA, I must then become a secretary. Maybe even *his* secretary. (Well I passed the exam, and years later played Alexis Carrington/Colby – a woman who had *male* secretaries!)

It was my father's firm belief that nothing is going to come to you unless you work for it that spurred me on and is the root of my own success. I had no expectations that things would just happen without my own dogged hard work. When I realised that nothing was going to be given to me on a plate, I knew I had to do everything in my power to make a success of my life.

My father believed that the more a person put into their life, the more they would get out of it. He believed, as I do, that we have no rights to anything in life, only opportunities that we must find and grasp. Today that is more true than ever. If you weren't brought up to have a strong work ethic by your parents, then you must choose a role model to emulate. Think of someone you truly admire, and make the example of that person, their life, achievements, ideals and goals the spur to *your* goals.

MY SECRETS

Reading biographies of well-known people who have achieved success through their efforts can stimulate your drive and imagination. Try to bring people into your life who are supportive, who praise you, help you, and make you feel good. Feeling good is only a step away from *doing* good, and doing good is well on the way to becoming successful. SO THINK BIG! Think successful. Take control.

Another of my parents' basic philosophies was that you have to take charge of yourself and control your own life. Often strong women who refuse to be bossed or pushed around are reviled as power-hungry bitches, because by standing up for ourselves and our rights, we offend and infuriate some people's notion of how women should behave.

If women truly acknowledge that the responsibility for their own lives rests with them they cannot afford to think of themselves simply as an adjunct to their parents, husbands/lovers or children. What women have to recognise is that if we want to be successful we *must* shed this 'I'm not really good enough' complex. We must have pride and self-respect, whether in our careers or at home, but we must be willing to work for it.

As well as the belief in hard work and self-reliance he instilled in me, my father also gave me a sense that I wasn't *quite* good enough. Like so many men of that era, he was a chauvinist of the old order, something familiar to many women of my generation. We were conditioned to believe we weren't as clever as men, that we couldn't accomplish what men accomplish, that we were basically inferior and needed a man to make us complete. Even though I was allowed to study at RADA, my father expected me to marry and settle down to a domestic life, with two point three children. From the word go, I rebelled against this concept, determined to succeed and to make something of myself. I wanted to prove my father wrong and show him I could make it on my own terms.

With my own children I tried to tread the fine line between telling them how wonderful they were, and instilling in them the values of hard work and self-reliance. Today there is a school of thought which says that children should be constantly told how wonderful they are and never scolded even if they play truant or decide not to do their homework. If a child is praised unconditionally day-in, day-out, I don't believe that child will have any motivation to work hard.

In my favourite hotel wearing my favourite suit, from Dior, during a promotional tour for my novel *Love, Desire and Hate*. The Ritz Hotel, Paris 1991.

MY SECRETS

There are no overnight successes. If you study any successful person, whether it be the owner of a high street chemist shop, working sixteen hours a day with parents, nieces and nephews to help; or Emma Thompson (an actress who started her career young and polished and honed her acting skills until she became a star in her early thirties), the truth is that success equals very hard work. Al Pacino, Robert de Niro, Vanessa Redgrave, Meryl Streep – all the actors whom we recognise as great talents are all known to work endless gruelling hours preparing for their roles. Dancers work excruciating hours; a ballet dancer's life is one of the toughest that exists. Sportsmen, footballers, writers, boxers, politicians, opera singers, doctors, lawyers, have all devoted hundreds of hours of hard work before they have found success. Therefore don't *you* deserve to devote a few hours to your own success in life? Your own goal achievement? You bet you do.

During the filming of *Dynasty* I was experiencing in my personal life some of the greatest traumas I had ever had to cope with. For seven and a half years, emotionally, physically and financially I was being drained to the nth degree, but I refused to allow my feelings of despair and frustration to get the better of me. I never brought my problems to the set, and no-one I worked with ever realised what kind of emotional upheaval I was going through.

Sometimes I would have to go on the set, as my character Alexis, totally in control, exquisitely dressed and coiffed, but having been awake all night dealing with one or more of the many dramas and tragedies that were unfolding in my own life.

I believe that you *must* separate what is going on in your personal life from your work and career. I never allowed my troubles to impinge on my work; therefore people could never understand, when I went through *two* messy and horrible divorces in this five-year period, that I actually had been in emotional turmoil for years. How stupid, I hear you say. Two divorces in five years, that's not what a clever or experienced woman would do. I agree, and as I have said before, mistakes can happen to anyone who jumps into life at the deep end, often with not enough thought. Anyway – that's *another* book!

One cannot bring one's personal problems to the workplace. Your problems belong at home, and you certainly won't achieve anything in your career and business life by sharing these unpleasant, and often

MY SECRETS

difficult occurrences with your workmates. Nobody really wants to know, and you appear weak if you allow your personal life to affect your work. World leaders don't bring their domestic dramas to Congress or Parliament, so why should you? We all know some whining drip who's always coming to work moaning about what her boyfriend/mother/ father has done to her and boring everyone to death. It's not important to other people and it is wasting their valuable time. In general they are not interested in your problems, so keep them to share with your best girlfriend or your dog, when they can be mulled over at length with a cup of tea and a box of Kleenex.

To be successful in whatever walk of life you choose, means that you *yourself* must be your *own* judge and your *own* critic. If I had relied on other people's opinions as to my performance as an actress or a writer, I would have quit while I was still a teenager. I had quite strong feminist views even then, and on marrying for the first time I blithely informed a journalist that as I was a busy working actress, in the studios for twelve or fourteen hours a day, I would not be doing any cooking, nor would I do the cleaning in my new little flat with my new big husband as I was far too occupied with my career.

Immediately a torrent of abuse from the tabloids poured on the head of this eighteen-year-old starlet.

Accusations that I was not a 'real woman', that what I was doing was 'against all the laws of nature' poured upon me. The impression the papers painted was of a headstrong girl thinking more of herself and her career than of her husband and unborn children. Well why not? Good heavens, I had only left school two years before! If you don't tend to your life and aspirations when you're young, I guarantee you nobody else is going to.

Although some people have tried to convince me otherwise, I have always felt that I was good at what I did. There is certainly no question that I would not have survived in this pitfall business had I not possessed a tremendous inner strength. I would have given up, fallen by the wayside as ninety-five per cent of my classmates at RADA did. They found acting too tough and demanding a profession so, one by one, they opted out. Considering myself and my wants has *not* made me a selfish person, and I have always cared deeply about my family, friends and the causes I support.

To travel hopefully is a better thing than to arrive, and the true success is to labour.

(ROBERT LOUIS STEVENSON)

So where does inner strength come from? We all possess it, but you have got to find it in yourself. As babies we have the strength to assert ourselves when we are hungry and want to be fed, to let the world know that we are wet and uncomfortable and our nappy needs changing. But too often that strength is squeezed out of us as we grow.

One of the things I've had to live with in the past fifteen years is that because the roles I've played have mostly been assertive, strong and ambitious women, the public's image of me is also that.

Having been brought up, like most women of my generation, to be a well-behaved, good little girl, the often unfavourable attitudes towards me, and the mixing up of my own persona with that of the character I was playing was sometimes distressing. So I decided to make the best of this situation and studied the character of Alexis to learn from her.

Trying to be liked is often the reason that women don't succeed in life – business men aren't always nice guys, why should you be? Alexis didn't care whether she was liked or not. I think she took it to extremes (after all this *was* a soap opera) but she always achieved her goals on *her* terms. To be a WINNER in life you must have plans and goals for yourself. I'm not advocating becoming a little Alexis, stomping over everybody with no consideration for their feelings, but I *am* saying that to have a successful life, you often have to put your *own* wants and desires before the demands of others.

Opposite: Jackie and I go over the top for Vanity Fair, 1988.

Joan Collins interviews Alexis Carrington. A trick photograph in which I play a journalist interviewing myself as an over-the-top-star. Acapulco, 1990.

. . .

You can learn more from failure than you can from success. If you are successful you rarely stop to analyse what *made* that success, that happiness, that moment, day, week, or month of supreme happiness and fulfilment. But through failure, whether it be failure in love, in work, in a relationship or in child rearing, we become introspective. We take a long hard look inside ourselves trying to discover what *didn't* make us tick.

'*Why* did he leave me?' or 'What did I do wrong that the boss/ teacher/parent/friend behaved so harshly to me?'

Success is infinitely sweeter if it comes to you later in life, and it's better, because then you will always have a goal to strive towards when

My first day on the set as Alexis in *Dynasty*. Little did I know that this was the beginning of a new and hugely successful chapter in my life. Hollywood, 1981.

Opposite: One of my first covers. I was being discovered as an English actress with glamour.

you're young. I am not talking about the kind of success that an actor, writer, or politician has. I am talking about success in *life*. The success that makes *you* a person other people want to be with, to share their confidences and laugh with, to be their friend. The success that makes you the woman who is hugged and loved by your family and told that you are wonderful. This is the true success of being a human being, not only to receive unconditional love from those you love, but to have it on *your* own terms. Not having to compromise yourself to other people's sometimes selfish wants, being loved *in spite* of your faults.

In a recent US study examining the mental health of women relating to the three factors of employment, marriage and children, it was found that single working women were in far better mental and physical shape than married women, with or without children, and single women, who had worked all their lives, were the most satisfied. A twenty-five year study of wives who didn't work revealed that not only did they have the lowest self-esteem of all women, but they considered themselves unattractive, incompetent, and suffered from an alarming array of illnesses – nervous breakdowns, heart palpitations, insomnia and unexplained feelings of guilt and shame. At the same time a study of single women found them not only healthier, wealthier and happier, and extremely content with their lot, but that they also had more regular sex!

The two biggest causes of depression in women were found to be low social status and marriage! Women who have never worked have the highest levels of depression. Family sociologist Jessie Bernard has said, 'Marriage may be hazardous to women's health.' But certainly not to men's. It has been proven that married men are far healthier, both mentally and physically, than bachelors.

It's obvious that marriage, which so many women crave, doesn't necessarily fulfil them, and that it can cause stress-related conditions.

So don't let the world intimidate you into tripping down that aisle and becoming the archetypal feminine woman, controlled by society, men and children. Do your own thing. If you are happily married good luck to you, and if you're not . . . well, you know what I would do! My favourite sage and wit, Oscar Wilde said, 'To love oneself is the beginning of a life-long romance.' It may take a bit of time – it did for me – but try it. It works!!

MY SECRETS

11 September, 1954

PICTURE
POST

JOAN COLLINS—
BRITISH FOR
GLAMOUR

4D

11 SEPTEMBER 1954

BRITAIN STAGES WORLD'S GREATEST AIR SHOW
A NEW PLAN FOR THE OVER SEVENTIES
ALEC GUINNESS SHOWS A GIRL ROUND PARIS

HULTON'S
NATIONAL
WEEKLY

VOL 64 • NO 11

CHAPTER FOUR

Less Stress

LEARNING TO MANAGE PRESSURE

IF AIDS IS the physical scourge of the 1990s, then the emotional and mental scourge is unquestionably stress. It is a debilitating, often life-threatening and most *definitely* beauty-robbing disease.

Unless one lives in a remote cottage far from civilisation one cannot escape stress. Our daily lives are assaulted by a barrage of stress-inducing sounds, sights, and situations which are unfortunately a normal part of late twentieth-century life. With the amenities we enjoy in modern civilisation, the profusion of food, material things, labour-saving devices, comes this downside.

Today our ears have become so inured to the constant assault of noise that we often barely notice it. For example, I was staying recently in a friend's glorious house in Acapulco, in an extremely unstressed atmosphere when, at lunch one day, someone commented on the loud whirring sound of the massive air-conditioning unit. 'How long has that been going?' he asked. 'It's *so* loud and intrusive.'

'It goes on *all* the time.' laughed my host. 'You just haven't noticed it.'

City life, with its cars, rumbling lorries and motorcycles, its hooting horns, pneumatic drills digging up the roads at practically every corner, radios and ghetto blasters blaring from vehicles or pedestrians, is an assault to the ears and a *major* cause of stress. Everywhere we go there are too many people: in shops, elevators, buses and trains, pushing and shoving, uncaring and rude.

There are simply never enough hours in the day, particularly for women, in these frenzied times we live in. However many new work-saving devices are invented – convenience foods, dishwashers, washing machines – we still seem to have *less* time to do the things we really want to do, than ever before.

No-one could get less stressed than this! St Tropez, 1992.

MY SECRETS

'I hate to say it, but the answer, I think, partly lies in that insidious little square box that sits in the living room. I have discovered if I don't turn television on during the day, even to listen to the news, I manage to achieve much more.

When Tara, Sacha and Katy were toddlers I severely rationed their television-viewing; they were allowed to watch for only one hour a day, which they could choose. I am convinced that this has helped them become much more creative in their adult lives. Now they hardly bother to watch television – even when I'm on!

. . .

Playing with Sacha and Katy in the garden of our house in Hampstead, 1974.

People who have a lot to do must be well-organised and organisation requires order. I can't bear a messy room, desk or dressing table, because I can't function properly in those circumstances.

Although everyone has the same amount of time in the day as the next person, why is it that some people seem to have more time to do things than others? I am always infuriated by rushing for an appointment to a doctor, dentist or lawyer, arriving on time and having to wait for twenty, thirty, sometimes even forty minutes. Doctors are always complaining that they don't have enough time. Yet they don't seem to mind keeping their patients waiting.

To a four-year-old, a year is a quarter of his life; to a forty-year-old it's a flash in the pan. As we grow older time seems to shrivel. You no sooner finish your summer holiday than it's time to start thinking about Christmas, and before you know it Christmas and all its fuss is upon us. When I was a child we used to start thinking about Christmas a week or two before it came. Certainly we never dreamed of buying presents for our family in October and November. But today, in some parts of America, Christmas decorations go up almost as soon as school starts after summer vacation – and the pressure to begin thinking about it is enormous. Magazines produce their Christmas issues in October and November and are packed with the hundreds of things you can make, special cookies you can bake, those fabulously elaborate table decorations with which you can amaze your family and friends. Then, immediately Christmas is over, there in those same magazines are bronzed bodies frolicking on sun-drenched Greek islands, inveigling you to book this hotel *now* for your summer holiday, or *you'll miss out*! The barrage of messages, both subliminal and overt, with which the average person is deluged adds to the feeling that time is racing by. So how do you slow down?

Go away to a peaceful place for a few days – it doesn't have to be a Mediterranean resort or a Caribbean island, it could be just a day getting away from it all in the country. Spend a day without newspapers, magazines, television, radio and traffic noise; away from the neighbours and the pressures of people telling you you've got to do this or you must do that.

There are many self-help books telling you how to manage your time correctly, how to divide it into the areas of family, work, social, or love life. Personally, I don't believe that anybody can really do this efficiently. We all live our life on the run: grabbing a sandwich here, throwing a load of laundry into the washing machine there, picking up children from school, racing home, often too tired even to prepare the nourishing dinners our mothers and grandmothers used to make.

Many of the problems that women face in their life today, stem from trying to balance what we *ourselves* want to do, and what others want *us* to do for them, partner, neighbours, children, relations, friends. We want to do one thing, and someone else expects, even manipulates, us to do something else. Because so many women have been brought up to try to please others, we often find ourselves put into situations where we are doing things for other people, and made to feel that we are failing as women if

Coping with telephones and business in my dressing room in the Warner Hollywood studios while shooting *Dynasty*.

MY SECRETS

we *don't* do these things.

We don't want to hurt the other person's feelings. We don't want to be rejected as a friend, neighbour or lover, so we grit our teeth and do what they want. How many times have you been told: 'If you don't do this, go there, make this, or make love, you don't really love/like me'?

We feel guilty if we refuse to do what is demanded of us but because we feel insecure, and underneath want to be liked, we too often just give in.

You do not have to be liked by everyone. There is an old saying that goes: 'You can please *some* of the people *all* of the time, and *all* of the people *some* of the time but you can't please *all* of the people *all* of the time.'

If you have young children, organising your time is especially difficult, but you *must* put aside some time each day for yourself. Whether it's after the children have gone to school, when the baby is sleeping, or in the lunch hour at work. Even if it's only a few minutes, steal it; it's your special time. You don't need an hour to eat. You can eat in five minutes, then find a quiet spot to lie or sit down, and try to let go of all your worries. Whether you are on a sofa, a chair, a park bench or on the grass, try to get away from outside pressures and *clear* your head.

On *Dynasty*, I used my lunch hour to do this, and when I'm not working, at about five or six o'clock in the evening, I open the windows, lie on my bed and listen to music or just stare into space. I try not to think or worry about anything, and after ten minutes of this I usually feel refreshed.

If your children are over the age of four or five why not get *them* to help you with the cooking, housework, cleaning and domestic tasks? I'm not advocating child labour here, but there is no question that toddlers can be put to a lot better use than sitting in front of a video game or television set all day. They can help you sort the laundry and have fun putting it in the machine. They can help you make simple things to eat in the kitchen, they can help with the washing up, and they can certainly start making their own beds. Teaching them young, making it fun for them will make them not only appreciate you more – but will give them a good grounding in *LIFE*!

Too many women are slaves to their children's needs without

realising that those children will be *far* better served in future life by learning everyday domestic tasks as toddlers. And Mummy can have some free time to herself, for her dreams, aspirations, beauty and health maintenance.

There are many stressful situations we have to cope with in our lifetime, many of which we cannot avoid: sitting exams, the death of a loved one, moving house, losing your job, having money worries, an illness or operation in the family, getting married, getting divorced, ending a relationship and even having a baby.

SOME SIMPLE RELAXATION TECHNIQUES

Think of your mind and body as a bank: when you work hard, play hard, or find yourself in stressful circumstances, you are making withdrawals from your bank. In order to stay healthy, you must replenish your bank's resources constantly.

One of the most important ways of doing this is to relax. If you find yourself tight-shouldered, hunched up, frowning, or making chewing motions with your mouth, you're probably suffering from stress.

The most effective method of relaxation I have learned takes only ten minutes: lie flat on the floor, stretch your whole body and become aware of everything from your toes to your fingertips, and then gradually relax each part of it and breathe very deeply. Feel every one of your muscles relax, loosen

How to completely relax in difficult circumstances, on the floor whilst filming in Amsterdam, 1991. Even dressed up and coiffed, I still manage to stretch out and de-stress for ten minutes.

MY SECRETS

up. Lie still for ten minutes, eyes closed, mind cleared of all thoughts. At the end of it you really should feel refreshed, relaxed and ready for anything.

My life is often extremely stressful so sometimes my method of relaxing is simply lying on my bed, watching TV or reading magazines. I need time to be by myself sometimes to get in tune with my inner self. I don't think we need the regular eight hours of sleep a night everyone says we do. Most people can function well on six or seven. If you spend only six hours sleeping, that gives you eighteen hours a day for other activities, and one of those activities can be helpful relaxation.

EXERCISE

Even if it's only walking, exercise is a great stress-reliever and tension reducer. If I must go up two flights of stairs, I always walk. I never take the lift because I feel so much better if I walk up.

MASSAGE

I have found massage to be deeply relaxing. It loosens up all the tension in the body, helps rid of it of toxins which have been stored in the muscles, and improves circulation. If you cannot afford to go to a professional masseur get your partner/friend to do it with you. All you need is a bed, a quiet room, with dim light and some massage oil. You can experiment on each other to find the most stress relieving points in your body, but a rule of thumb is to start massaging the head and finish with the back or to start with the back and finish with the head.

AROMATHERAPY

Aromatherapy combines Western massage with Eastern pressure point techniques. The treatment consists of massaging the whole body with essential oils, sometimes in different combinations. Essential oils are especially chosen to suit each individual's need, and can be used either to relax or stimulate: for example, sandalwood is a very relaxing oil whereas geranium has a stimulating and uplifting effect. They are absorbed into the bloodstream and can be used as homeopathic remedies. This is a delicious way of being massaged, which I used to have done professionally on matinée days in between performances of *Private Lives*. But it should *only* be done by a professional.

Three can do it, too!

MY SECRETS

REFLEXOLOGY

The principle of reflexology is that each part of the body, such as a hand or foot, or a finger, reflects the whole body, and that different parts affect particular areas of the body. Stiffness, tenderness or pain in any of these zones may indicate that the corresponding organ is not functioning at peak level. Many reflexologists claim that it is one of the most powerful alternative therapies, and an instant de-stresser. I have found it beneficial for headaches, minor back pain, and stress relief.

SHIATSU

Shiatsu has developed over five thousand years from an ancient Chinese tradition. Unlike other forms of massage, it does not involve kneading the muscles. It follows the same principles as acupuncture, but uses touch instead of needles, working on and unblocking the channels of energy that flow through the body by putting pressure on specific points (or meridians).

I don't practise them, but yoga and meditation are also other forms of relaxation that many people swear by.

PAMPERING

I believe that in order to be able to relax, you must create a soothing environment which you are comfortable with.

The couturier, Valentino, who lives more beautifully than practically anyone I know, is rumoured to have once said that he would rather starve than eat off an ugly plate! We don't need to go to such extremes but we can all improve the world around ourselves if we decide to think positively and creatively and make the effort in our surroundings.

It is essential to pamper yourself if you want to relax, but pampering yourself isn't necessarily expensive. To have three or four pillows on your bed instead of one is not going to break the bank; neither is having extra blankets, nor a hot water bottle when it's cold. The little things in life add up to the big picture of a comforting, relaxing environment, in which all your accumulated stress just melts away.

MY SECRETS

CHAPTER FIVE

The Best Ways to Age

DON'T BE IN A HURRY ABOUT IT

STAYING ALIVE

LET'S SAY YOUR life is a three-act play. The first act is from birth to approximately age thirty – the youthful years. The second is from thirty to sixty – the middle years. The third is from age sixty onwards. The first two acts of most plays are usually good, but the third act is usually the best. Therefore your life should be as full of feeling, action, power, and drama as you can possibly make it, and it *can* be possible.

Of course, not everything about ageing is so great. Diminishing eyesight, loss of hearing and loss of short-term memory, aren't a million laughs, but because we are born with more than ten billion brain cells (that's an *awful* lot of brain cells), modern research now believes that losing brain cells as you get older is not as bad a situation as was once thought and therefore intelligence doesn't *have* to decline. How you feel, and what you do with your life is up to *you*. Genes, heredity and your family's health history can play a great part in your longevity, but the many examples of fit, athletic people over fifty are making the world notice how older people today are changing. This is the first generation to have enough knowledge to have a *practical* chance of staying younger than ever, for longer.

In California, where the quest for youth has become almost an obsession, a cult has developed of people who, when they die, have their bodies frozen and kept in special temperature-controlled rooms for the amount of years it will take for scientists to eventually discover a way to either make them 'young' again, or cure the disease they died of.

MY SECRETS

But getting older should not carry a stigma. It should be a badge people wear with pride and dignity. With each year that passes, we should achieve more, and if we take proper care of ourselves, there is nothing to stop us looking and feeling our optimum best.

THE WISDOM OF YEARS

Certain cultures revere older people enormously. Jewish society has always done so, as have the Italians. The Japanese who truly venerate their elders have one of the highest life expectancies in the world. So why not? It makes sense that if you are admired, respected and listened to, you *want* to live as long and as fully as you possibly can. What people don't seem to realise is that the youthful period – the time in one's life when supposedly one does the most, achieves the most, and is the most desirable – is extremely short: from eighteen to about thirty-three. After that we've all got nearly a half century to go. Let's live it to the hilt!

Since most people's middle age is the longest time of their lives, why not make it the best time? Sadly, our society has a tradition of chucking old people on the slag heap. Today the young think they know practically everything and many disdain anything old-fashioned, that has history, tradition, conservatism. But everything new and modern is *not* necessarily good.

I was first made aware of my own ageing and mortality when I was twenty-five. Dating a younger man of twenty-three, I was referred to in some magazines as an 'older woman'! We both thought this perfectly ridiculous, but it hardly bothered me – after all I was in the prime of my youth, wasn't I?

However, I was under contract to Twentieth Century Fox studios, and was beginning to receive subtle signals that I was no longer as young as I *should* be by their standards. When I received the script of *Sons and Lovers* in which the character I was to play was described as an 'older woman', I turned down the part (subsequently played by Mary Ure), and went on suspension of salary for three months. From that moment I have always thought that this older woman stuff was a load of baloney. (A cynic once said the best way to look younger is to lie about your age! He was a college lecturer who told everyone he was eighty, but was in fact only seventy!)

Wrinkles should merely indicate where the smiles have been.

(MARK TWAIN)

MY SECRETS

We don't have enough positive images of older women in this country. The French, for example, have always admired older women far more, hence they have role models like Catherine Deneuve, Jeanne Moreau and the late Simone Signoret. In America it wasn't until Linda Evans, Diahann Carroll and myself appeared in *Dynasty* that it became generally accepted that over forty was *not* over the hill, and that youth was not the only game in town.

Today I do not see myself as locked in a time warp trying to act and look younger. I enjoy life – all aspects of it: my family, friends, my career, and travel – but the main thing I have noticed about myself is that I am much calmer, more patient, more serious and more tolerant. In fact, I'm nicer!

Men in our society, over forty, fifty or even sixty are of course still considered to be attractive and desirable, whereas women are generally not. I am delighted however to see these attitudes changing.

Today there are thousands of fabulous and energetic women over fifty in all walks of life. The list of celebrities is virtually endless: Shirley Maclaine, Stephanie Powers, Kate O'Mara, Linda Gray, Tina Turner, Sophia Loren, Shirley Bassey, Elizabeth Taylor, Lauren Hutton, Angela Lansbury, Arlene Dahl, Pamela Harriman, Barbara Streisand, whose voice just gets better and better. The number of vital, intelligent, active, ambitious women over fifty, sixty and even seventy is growing, and I want to see *more* women on that list! I want *more* women over fifty to feel their lives have meaning and joy and love in them. I want to know that there are more women out there who have as much a sense of purpose in their life at fifty as they did at twenty-five.

So what can we do to halt the ageing process? Being positive, happy, and fulfilled certainly keeps people younger and more vibrant, and people who *look* younger than they are, generally *feel* younger than they are, and they also usually attract people who are younger than they are, not just as lovers but as friends too.

It's up to you of course. *You* have to wage your own personal battle with the ravages of time, but old age *will* creep up on you unless you are prepared to combat it. Compulsive dieters, food faddists and exercise freaks, who deprive themselves of the deliciously sinful bit of chocolate or a satisfying glass of wine, tend to look more stressed out, more haggard, and less attractive than those who are more *laissez-faire*

Do not resist getting old – many are denied the privilege.

(ANON)

MY SECRETS

about life. I have always believed that a little of what you fancy does you good.

It takes guts; it takes determination, persistence and commitment, but above all it takes an understanding that *you* are the lead character in your own life story, and if anybody is going to do anything to change your life it *can* only be you.

You cannot of course have the skin of a twenty-two-year-old when you are forty-five. Neither can you run up two flights of stairs, nor dance without getting breathless in discos all night as you did as a teenager, and wake up the next morning feeling fresh, alert and ready to do it all over again. There are limits to one's energy levels, and young people can burn the candle at both ends, *and* in the middle, and have no adverse morning after feelings. But as we grow older we can't. That's why we *must* take more care of ourselves both nutritionally and exercise-wise as we age.

Older women have been stereotyped, caricatured and categorised as unappealing for far too long. We've had enough of those endless mother-in-law jokes that music hall comedians used to spout, those silly seaside postcards always depicting some fat unattractive old biddy, with her skirt blowing up above her head looking foolish. It's time that society allowed older women to be as much of a force in society as older men and younger people.

THE APPLIANCE OF SCIENCE

In my last book I used the example of the Queen Mother as an extraordinary woman over eighty. Today she's still exceptional. I sat behind Barbara Cartland on a plane to Nice one day and was amazed at her vitality and vivacity. She never stopped talking, and strolled down the steps of the plane like a woman thirty years younger. Obviously Barbara Cartland lives with passion; a passion not only for love, but for the sheer joy of being alive. If you live *every day* of your life with passion, and are determined to enjoy it to the utmost, you may get older chronologically but you won't have let age defeat you. People who are passionate about their work are also passionate about their play; whether it is sports, travelling, reading, making cakes, going for walks, making collages, or collecting stamps.

Life goes by fast – much too fast. We are like photographs in an

Man is young as long as he can repeat his emotions, woman as long as she can inspire them.

(OSCAR WILDE)

album or a book on the library shelf, taken down, borrowed, and then put back – a flickering image of an old black and white movie. The artist Francis Bacon said, 'Life is but a short interval between birth and death, and of course it is totally absurd!' I don't know about that, but I do know that we should make the most of every millisecond.

One of the views passed down to us is that as we get older we are going to degenerate. That means losing our looks, slowing down physically and mentally (for instance our eyes lose their focus and appetite diminishes), and eventually perhaps getting some form of long-term illness – cancer, arthritis, heart disease. At the opposite extreme is the belief that the miracles of modern science may be able to stave off every single thing that goes wrong with us, lengthening our life span ad infinitum. Look at that Californian obsession with prolonging youth and life. Although I believe that we must accept growing older, I see no reason for us to lose our looks as we do so. Who says only young things can be beautiful? Of *course*, degenerative diseases will happen to some of us – it's inevitable. Even though science has become much more skilled in *preventing* many debilitating diseases, the curse of our civilisation is that so many diseases that were unheard of when man lived a simpler life, and ate a simpler and more basic balanced diet, now occur regularly.

A baby born today will probably live to be around eighty years old, whereas a baby born in 1900 would only live to be fifty. This is because science has reduced infant mortality so that average life expectancy has increased. In fact we have little chance of existing any longer than our grandfathers did unless we take extra special care of ourselves, and the way we live. Another theory is that there is a huge difference between their chronological and their biological ages. For example my father, born in 1903, lived to be eighty-five, which certainly would not have been expected at the time of his birth. He was a vigorous healthy man who married again after my mother died, and had another daughter when he was well into his sixties. He enjoyed his life completely, and it was only when he *stopped* savouring it that I saw him wither away and die. He simply didn't want to be around any more.

I recently discovered some surprising statistics about how long we live. The average lifespan in Rome 2000 years ago was twenty-two

If youth is a fault it is one which is soon corrected.

(GOETHE)

years! In 1850 it was only forty. At the turn of the century it was fifty. In 1945 it was sixty-seven and today it is seventy-three. The Bible tells us that Moses lived to be 120 and Methuselah 969 years, although nobody has yet proven such a fact. I wonder what the maximum lifespan of man would be if he took care of himself perfectly!

Some believers say we *could* live to be a 120! Hunza, an isolated kingdom in the Himalayas, is a country without disease, in which many people live to be 125 years old! Some of the men have been known to sire children at the age of 100, and the average life expectancy is ninety! The Hunza people have an unstressed life. They eat a low animal-protein diet (which researchers now believe to be one of the keys to reverse the ageing process) and drink natural water which is high in essential vitamins. They are free from the hazards of pollution, and refined, processed, poisoned foods, and they work extremely hard even when older.

You are never in control on the back of a bike!

Today although we live in a so-called politically-correct society it seems that only ageing is thought of negatively. We all use negative epithets to describe the old: wrinklie, crabby, senile, frail; older women trying to appear younger are called mutton-dressed-as-lamb, crone, witch, hag.

I prefer positive images: matriarch or patriarch, the older, revered person who occupies a position at the head of the family and is respected and admired by all; the wise man or woman, spiritually at peace with themselves, sharing their experience and knowledge with others. We should appreciate that older people can be perceptive, philosophical, nurturing, morally concerned, graceful and unafraid. Noel Coward said he was stimulated and deeply impressed by 'the charm of old age when it was allied to health, and intelligence.'

Ageing is perceived as being a steady decline in physical and mental functions from youth onwards. If we accept this decline, a

MY SECRETS

person in their seventies must by definition be less virile, healthy and strong than a person in their forties or fifties. However, this describes only what is typical and average among older people in our badly exercised, ill-nourished and sedentary society.

It doesn't have to be like that. People who eat properly and exercise consistently well into their seventies and eighties, can be just as powerful and as full of life as younger people. Visualise yourself as how you want to be. If you really want to be strong, healthy and younger-looking you can be. But if you think of yourself as decrepit and on the slippery slope to senility, you will be. How often have you heard someone say, 'What can you expect, I am getting older,' or 'Of course I can't climb up all those stairs, I'm over fifty.'? Rubbish! *Think* yourself younger and healthier and you will feel better and more vigorous.

Now take a good hard look at yourself in the mirror. List your good qualities on one side of a piece of paper, and your bad qualities on the other. You will probably find that you have far fewer bad qualities than you have good. That's great because our good qualities are what people notice in us.

HORMONE REPLACEMENT THERAPY

This magic formula has given a new lease of life to millions of women over the age of forty, even though there has been controversy about it. Many doctors believe it is detrimental; however, when taken with a doctor's approval the benefits can be enormous.

When the ovaries stop making oestrogen, which usually happens either after a major operation (for example a hysterectomy), or menopause, the bones rapidly start to lose their density. Within twenty years, many women between the ages of forty-five and seventy-five have lost about thirty per cent of their skeletal structure. What a horror that is. Have you ever seen those old women tottering around Greece or Spain, bowed over from the waist, their skins leathery and pouched, their tiny bones frail and bird-like? You see more women like this than men of a similar age because nature's way of playing yet another one of her nasty tricks on women is that we start losing our bone density earlier than men.

After the menopause, this loss accelerates and the dreaded disease osteoporosis can occur, which can, however, be largely kept at bay by

This dress was actually two sizes too big for me. It's pinned in the back with huge safety-pins for this shot. *Decadence* 1993.

taking Hormone Replacement Therapy. Many doctors are still wary of HRT. They just shake their heads unsympathetically, and say that women must endure the unpleasant side effects of the change of life as they have had to for centuries. What nonsense! In 1994 I don't think *any* woman should have to endure *anything* that can be prevented, and with a doctor's blessing there is no reason to have to suffer any of those irritating and annoying symptoms that happen after a certain age.

Some women of course experience none of these things, but there are unfortunate women who have such uncomfortable night sweats, hot flushes, palpitations, and other dreadful and embarrassing side effects, that they are driven almost to the point of madness. HRT stops all that. It also improves the quality and elasticity of the skin, the hair, restores sexual libido and energy, and can give a woman many more productive, fulfilling and ailment-free years.

As children we probably all knew an older aunt, or a middle-aged woman who seemed a little dotty. That was probably the result of the horrible changes her body was forcing her to go through. It's called a natural function, but so is having cramps. Today, no woman would think of suffering monthly cramps without taking something to alleviate them. So why not take something that is going to alleviate the problems of menopause?

There can be some harmful side-effects of taking HRT, one of them being that oestrogen can cause the build-up of womb lining, and although it is not actually cancerous it can become so without regular check ups. It has also been thought in some medical circles that HRT can accelerate the growth of small cancers in the breast, so mammograms or regular self-examination are advised for women taking it, particularly if you have a family history of breast cancer. Thrombosis is also a minor threat to women taking HRT, especially if they are heavy smokers or considerably overweight. Because it is still extremely controversial, doctors have not yet reached full agreement about whether HRT does or does not contribute to breast cancer. However, since doctors seldom totally agree about anything, I would suggest that with proper care you should do what *you* think is best for yourself.

There is no medical proof yet which shows that HRT has any bearing on cervical and ovarian cancer.

However there is absolutely nothing in life that is 100 per cent

MY SECRETS`

safe. The birth control pill, which millions of women have been taking for years, is definitely not 100 per cent safe, neither is the condom nor even having a baby. So why should we expect any pill to be 100 per cent safe?

Many people think that HRT is something that has been invented in the past decade, but in America some women, now in their eighties, have been taking it for nearly thirty years. In comparing a group of American women over the age of seventy-five who took HRT, with a group of women of the same age who did not, doctors found an incredible difference in their health, vitality and general well-being.

I am certainly not saying that *all* women need to take HRT. There are millions of women over forty-five who don't take it and who are in excellent health and spirits. But there is a better chance of not getting fractures as you get older if you have taken HRT than if you have not.

HRT is not a total miracle. It's not going to make you live to a hundred, it's not going to make you look twenty-five again, but doctors who *are* in favour of this controversial treatment have stated unequivocally that it *can* keep you out of the hospital, out of the divorce courts, and out of the madhouse.

Always remember that *you* are at the helm of your life. Don't let your doctor brush you off, as some have done, when you want to make the quality of your life after a certain age better. Don't let him bully you, and if he categorically says you shouldn't take HRT go and see another doctor for a second opinion!

Similarly, I have always believed strongly in the benefits of vitamin C, and in New York when pregnant with my first child, eagerly told my American doctor that I was going to be taking lots of it.

'How ridiculous,' he laughed. 'You might as well eat a candy bar for all the good vitamin C is going to do for you and the baby.'

I took no notice of what he said, and I took masses of vitamin C, still do, and of course recent research and theories have proven that it is extremely beneficial – so your doctor may not always be right.

*N*o *woman should ever be quite accurate about her age. It looks so calculating.*

(OSCAR WILDE)

CHAPTER SIX

You are What You Eat

FOOD FOR THOUGHT

THERE HAVE PROBABLY been more words written about dieting than anything else – other than sex. Virtually every woman has, at some point in her life, been on a diet. I have dieted on and off for years, and I've come to the conclusion that diets just don't work. They may work for a week, or a month, sometimes even for six months, but in the end people tend to go back to their old eating habits and those pounds pile on inexorably once more.

We are all too obsessed with our shapes. There is really no such thing as the ideal female body shape in the 1990s. Although there is far more tolerance of different body shapes now than there was in the 1970s and 1980s, I wonder why so many fashion photographers still insist on using stick-thin models?

A few months ago *Vogue* featured a teenage waif model, in underwear, looking like a fugitive from Belsen. What a sad indictment of how we expect our young women to look today.

In the 1960s we emulated Jean Shrimpton and Twiggy, and some of us dieted ourselves to a frazzle to try and obtain their perfect thinness. It is hardly surprising that anorexia nervosa has become so widespread among young girls – some as young as eight. Why is being skinny our ideal of beauty? One of the most attractive women on television is the comedienne Dawn French, a woman who could never be described as slim, but who is comfortable with her size and looks. Because of this she is even more attractive. I know too many women of the sort aptly described by the writer Tom Wolfe as social x-rays.

Never eat more than you can lift.

(MISS PIGGY)

MY SECRETS

These forty-five to seventy-year-old women are starved and exercised until they look like a scrawny bag of bones. There is nothing attractive about looking like that, and although fashion designers insist on showing their clothes on tall, slender girls in their teens and early twenties, the average woman must be sensible, and realise that she can *never* look like that, indeed never did look like that, even when she was young. I like to see women who look like women – with breasts and hips and a bit of roundness.

Today the gorgeous supermodels Helena Christenson, Claudia Schiffer and Cindy Crawford who have replaced Hollywood stars as the aspirational role models for young women are still far from looking like an ordinary woman. When I was a young girl everybody wanted to look like a movie star, but those stars had a look more real than today's models. Women like Lana Turner, Ava Gardner, Marilyn Monroe, Elizabeth Taylor and Rita Hayworth were mostly of average height and by no means skinny. They all had full bosoms, slim waists, curvaceous hips and solid legs, and with make-up, hairstyles and clothes it wasn't too difficult for us and our mothers to try and achieve their look. Attempting to look like Linda Evangelista, on the other hand, is akin to impossible even if you're twenty-five.

· · ·

You are what you eat. I know this is true because a great part of the way I look and feel is because of my dietary habits. After I had my first child I gained nearly thirty pounds and it was tough to lose. But I persevered with exercise and educating myself on proper nutrition and developing healthy eating habits. I was quite uncomfortable for several months after the birth, as I hated being overweight. It didn't suit my lifestyle – my clothes didn't fit, and my energy level was extremely low. When I finally lost the twenty-eight pounds I had gained I vowed I would never allow myself to gain that weight again.

You don't have to be a diet junkie to live healthily and have a good figure – what you must do is eat a sensible *balanced* diet. If you eat chocolate pudding one day, you should balance that the next day with a papaya or mango for dessert. If you drink wine one night, then only drink Evian water the next day. You can't live on white fish and health foods forever – you'd die of boredom.

MY SECRETS

I believe in enjoying life to the full, which means that if I am given a box of chocolates I'll indulge myself, *but* I will make up for that indulgence the next day. Although I think a certain amount of plumpness looks good, and that the skinny look is passé, being fat isn't my ideal of what is beautiful.

Real obesity is as unattractive as the scrawny stick-thin women in New York who live on carrots and water. I don't understand how people can be proud of being unhealthily fat and continually justify it as some do. This seems to me to be a self-destructive and negative response to the problem.

Instead of dieting to lose weight you must start developing healthy eating habits. There are of course all kinds of diets for losing weight fast when you want to get ready for some special event, wedding, holiday, or party for which you want to fit into a particular dress. Crash diets *can* make you lose weight fast, if you stick to one totally. But how boring to live your life counting calories, having to look forward to a wilted lettuce leaf and a few miserable carrots, when you could be eating delicious and nutritional meals. With crash dieting all you are doing is depriving yourself of one of life's greatest pleasures.

Food is certainly one of the delights of my life – but only good food. I am totally uninterested in junk food and I have trained myself to avoid food that has little nutritional value. Now, on the whole, my body obeys my mind. Occasionally I cheat with the odd piece of chocolate or even a *box* of chocolates and of course I do have a piece of cake at birthday parties.

In general my basic eating plan consists of the following:

BREAKFAST

One or two cups of (instant) coffee (infinitely better for you than the filter or decaffeinated kind), with low fat milk and either brown sugar or Canderel. I am not a huge believer in saccharin-type sweeteners, as I have read of rats dying from large doses of them, but I don't consider two or three tiny lumps of Canderel a day can cause too much harm.

A tablespoon of APIS Royal Jelly tonic if I am on a course of it.

If I'm not working, I'm not usually hungry until lunch time, but when filming I have one or two pieces of wholewheat toast with Flora

Beauty provoketh thieves sooner than gold.

(WILLIAM SHAKESPEARE)

A healthy breakfast.
On tour with *Private Lives* in
Miami, 1991.

MY SECRETS

and marmalade, and a glass of freshly squeezed orange juice. I wouldn't dream of having longlife orange juice that comes out of a carton, which to me has the vitamin value of a Jaffa cake.

LUNCH AND DINNER

At home, lunch is either a can of sardines (with all the oil), and a couple of sliced tomatoes; a tuna fish salad with low-fat mayonnaise; or a salad of broccoli, cauliflower, peppers, lettuce, tomatoes, cucumbers, parsley and rocket. (I put whatever is in the fridge in the salad and eat it with, I must admit, a lot of olive oil and lemon juice dressing and a couple of crispbreads or Ryvita which have fewer than fifty calories each). Another variation might be two hard-boiled eggs mashed up with low-fat mayonnaise, a tomato, two low-fat crispbreads or tsatziki which is a Greek dish made with yoghurt, garlic and cucumber.

If I lunch at a restaurant I usually have asparagus, which is particularly nutritious, whenever it is in season, or a rocket or mixed salad. For the main course I tend to have something like smoked salmon and scrambled eggs, grilled sole and fresh vegetables, pasta or risotto. (Pasta *primavera* is one of my favourite dishes. See recipe on page 170.)

I never have red meat at lunch, and in fact I will only eat it if it is served at a dinner party. Fortunately most hosts are aware that red meat is not good for you and serve veal or chicken, or fish.

Having desserts is cyclical with me. Sometimes I eat them, sometimes I don't. I am about half a stone heavier now than when I was in *Dynasty*, but I am aware that after a certain age the face needs to be a little fuller than it does in the twenties and thirties.

But what about snacks, I hear you say, the downfall of everyone, particularly those who stay at home with young children? I believe that if snacks aren't in the house, you're not going to crave them. If I know that I have even the *tiniest* piece of chocolate in the house, by four o'clock, when my blood sugar is low and I'm feeling peckish, I will root it out like a dog searching for a bone. Then I devour it with that delicious feeling of guilt one always has when one is doing something that one knows is wrong. Now that my children are not living at home, the contents of my fridge consist of low-calorie things: hard-boiled eggs, broccoli, cucumbers and cauliflower. I also snack on yoghurt, bananas,

MY SECRETS

melon or other fruits such as papaya or mango.

Since I often eat in restaurants, I am lucky enough to be able to choose what I want to eat from a menu. But in the summer at my house in the South of France, we eat extremely healthy and well-balanced meals. Some of the recipes you will find at the end of this book.

We don't necessarily put on weight *only* because of what we eat. What we drink is much more calorie-laden than we realise. I drink wine, champagne, and coffee, so I'm probably taking in at least a quarter of my daily amount of calories this way. I know I am not setting a good example, but it makes me happy. If I drink a little more I just eat a little less.

Here are some of my tips to stop you eating too much:

□ Brush your teeth with peppermint toothpaste if you're feeling peckish. You won't feel so hungry with freshly-cleaned teeth.

□ Chew low sugar gum – or eat a boiled sweet – only about twenty calories each.

□ If you must drink wine – a spritzer is particularly good: only forty calories a glass.

□ Always leave something on your plate, even if you were brought up to finish everything.

□ Try to skip desserts – they're the killer.

□ Eat little and often. Some people need three meals a day. If you are one of them – have them, but make them *small* meals.

□ Stop nibbling! Nuts, crisps and cocktail savouries are the worst. I know they're my downfall so I try to stay away from them.

□ Cut out salt and salty food like pickles, smoked salmon and sausages.

□ Cut out everything stodgy; puddings, pies, buns, doughnuts, white bread.

□ Remember if every time you crave something sweet you eat an apple or a piece of broccoli, after a few days your appetite will have adjusted and the craving will stop.

□ A craving for sweets is an addiction – just like cigarettes. Try to wean yourself off with fruit.

Although I don't advocate eating sweets, for birthdays I always make an exception!

MY SECRETS

CHAPTER SEVEN

Supplementary Benefits

ESSENTIAL VITAMINS

SOME PEOPLE TAKE megadoses of vitamins and minerals for years, assuming that if a little is good for you, a lot must be better, but there is no evidence to support this, as a study released recently in America proved. Some doctors believe that you can get all the vitamins and minerals you need from the correct diet. But there are many reasons why we cannot rely on our diet alone to give us all the vitamins, minerals and micronutrients we need:

Food today is so highly processed that deterioration of vitamins in food occurs, and the water we boil vegetables in and throw away often has more nutrients in it than the vegetables themselves. Most people don't really like foods that are good for them. Since people do not eat what they hate it is impossible to recommend a standard diet. Storage of foods, as well as overprocessing, reduces the vitamin content, especially vitamin E. Smoking and drinking alcohol and caffeine to excess and taking birth control pills, aspirin and laxatives, all deplete vitamins and minerals.

The polluted atmosphere in most metropolitan cities can rob our body of much needed vitamins.

I believe strongly in the benefits of vitamins and I recommend the following:

☐ *For stress* Vitamin B.
☐ *For cholesterol* Cod liver oil and lethicin.

□ *For menopause* Evening primrose oil and Vitamin E.
□ *For protection against colds and cancer and for the immune system* Vitamin C.
□ *For sleep* Calcium and magnesium.
□ *For skin diseases* Vitamin A.

Here are some of the most important and beneficial vitamins:

VITAMIN A has been called the vision vitamin as it is essential for healthy eyesight. It is also excellent for anti-infection, for growth and healing. It is one of the best vitamins for the skin because it helps keep the skin soft and smooth, protecting it against dryness, the formation of wrinkles and irregular pigmentation and it maintains the mucous membranes. A proper supply of vitamin A protects the body against infection because it strengthens skin cell walls. It is found in green and yellow vegetables, milk, some fruits, liver, and egg yolks. It can help arthritis, and skin diseases such as psoriasis, acne and eczema. It has also been known to slow the ageing of cellular material, and possibly help inhibit cancer by enhancing the production of white blood cells. A deficiency of vitamin A can cause night-blindness, inflammation of the eyes and eyelids, brittle nails, poor skin and hair, fatigue, diarrhoea. It can also diminish our bodies' ability to use vitamin C. It is however essential not to overdose on this vitamin as it can be toxic.

ANTIOXIDANTS – vitamins C and E and beta carotene – are the 'stars' of the vitamin world and among the fastest-selling of all vitamins. Antioxidants help limit the spread of degenerative illnesses, cancer and premature ageing and can prevent heart disease by preventing the build-up of cholesterol. Antioxidants also protect cells by binding electrically unbalanced free radicals. Carrots are an excellent source of beta carotene, citrus fruits for vitamin C, and vegetable oils are full of vitamin E. Selenium also has antioxidant qualities. Now heart experts believe that antioxidants can help cholesterol in coronary arteries, as oxidisation is part of what causes them to be blocked.

MY SECRETS

BETA CAROTENE is found in fruits such as cantaloupe, apricots, peaches, and vegetables such as broccoli, squash, spinach, and tomato juice. It is now universally recognised for cancer and heart disease prevention.

VITAMIN B6. Bananas, avocados, chicken and potatoes are all on the B6 list, as are spinach, green peas, walnuts and wheatgerm. Vitamin B is essential for people who are irritable, highly strung, overworked and have memory problems.

VITAMIN C is considered a major preventative for colds. (I take a mega dose of vitamin C a day, and I only get one slight cold every two or three years, which is usually because I have not been taking care of myself or have been working too hard.) Vitamin C plays a major role in sustaining body immunity, helping to protect us from free radicals and oxidising chemicals which are known to cause cancer. It helps to block formation of blood clots and protects against heart attacks. It is essential for effective assimilation of iron, calcium, and other minerals, and it actually helps to regulate cholesterol levels. You can increase your calcium and magnesium intake by eating more whole grains, green vegetables, cultured dairy products, nuts and seeds, eggs, cheese and legumes and by cutting down on red meat.

The scientist Dr Linus Pauling has always believed that vitamin C reduces the risk of *all* types of cancer. Unfortunately the medical profession, both in Britain and America, has not yet truly accepted his theory, but some of the medical journals have already published articles in which they have linked vitamin C deficiency with cancer and heart disease.

Osteoporosis, the progressive thinning of the bones, is attributed to declining oestrogen levels and a low intake of calcium and magnesium. I take a daily dose of calcium in pill form. (The recommended dose is 800 mgs.)

VITAMIN D is found in sunlight. As we all know, those of us who live in this sceptred isle don't get enough of that, so it is important to get more, from either multiple vitamins, or cod liver oil. I used to have to take a tablespoon of cod liver oil every night when I was a

child. I hated taking it at the time but my mother must have known something because I have always been relatively healthy. Now you can buy cod liver oil or shark liver oil tablets which you swallow, so you don't have its horrible aftertaste.

We need vitamin D to regulate and metabolise calcium. It is also needed to maintain our nervous system and skin. The foods which contain the highest amount of vitamin D are sardines, dairy products, egg yolks and, much as I hate to admit it, organ meats. Since direct sunlight and meat from the organs of animals are bad for us, it is obviously more important to take a supplement, and I would suggest 400 international units a day, or you can drink a quart of milk (not recommended for the over-twenties).

V I T A M I N E has been known for many years as the sex vitamin. However, whether that is true or not, there is no question that vitamin E is vitally important for women, both in our diets and as a supplement.

It helps the immune system, it is essential for the maintenance of all tissue, and for healthy blood circulation, and it is one of the best antioxidants.

It can reverse the ageing process, and help keep you younger longer.

Recently it has been shown that vitamin E can reduce the incidence of tumours and breast lumps, lower cholesterol and toxic substances in the body and hence slow down the ageing process. It can be found in wheatgerm, soyaflower and sunflower oils, soya beans, dark green vegetables, nuts, brown rice and unsaturated oils.

If I had to take only one vitamin it would be a difficult choice between E and C.

MY SECRETS

CHAPTER EIGHT

Fit for Life

FOR YEARS EXERCISE has been touted as the panacea for all ills: the more the better; the harder it is to do the better you'll feel. Feel the burn! No pain, no gain! That philosophy has changed in the 1990s.

Patrick Nagel was a healthy thirty-eight-year-old artist who performed in a celebrity aerobics charity show and died later that same night. I'm not saying that what happened to my friend can necessarily happen to you, but there is no question that exercise *without* the proper limbering up or preparation can be fatal.

With the wrong exercise you can often do yourself a very serious injury indeed, particularly if your muscles have not been warmed up. I myself have strained ligaments and muscles in the past even *with* structured warm-ups. The number of gyms and exercise gurus whose insurance policies have increased by over a hundred per cent in the past five years owing to accident and injury is legion.

The truth is that exercise programmes should vary for everyone, as everyone is different. What works for a nubile eighteen-year-old girl is not going to work for a forty-five-year-old housewife. You don't have to totally knock yourself out at the gym any more. Experts now think that *moderate* exercise for women is preferable to struggling, sweating and generally overdoing it. You no longer need to get up at dawn to jog through smoggy streets, or stretch and strain an hour a day at the gym.

The best and easiest exercise of all is, of course, walking. I don't mean a slouchy stroll whilst doing some window shopping. I mean brisk walking for a steady mile or two with shoulders back, chin up and breathing properly. Walking increases the heart rate, lowers insulin levels and increases the amount of oxygen that reaches the cells all over the body. It also helps in the elimination of wastes which can cause free radical damage.

I firmly believe that exercise can definitely make you look and feel

MY SECRETS

younger, and help you live longer. It has been proved by studying groups of people over a period of several decades, that regular exercise definitely delays the ageing process; it firms the muscles, keeps the body younger looking and of course improves self-image and gives you a goal to achieve for yourself. It prevents and reduces obesity, lowers blood pressure and helps combat anxiety and depression. It improves mental functions, heightens vitality, improves oxygen-carrying capacity of the blood, increases lean muscles, strengthens bones and prevents osteoporosis. It also improves and strengthens the heart, makes the skin look and feel younger and lowers triglycerides.

Regular exercise performed all your life will not only help prevent heart disease, but can also prevent early death from cardiovascular

The Cinzano commercials were very successful on television, and my leg exercises were proved beneficial.

disease, stroke and respiratory disease. But, and this is a big but, it has *got* to be done regularly. You *cannot* exercise for one hour one week, and then do nothing for the next month. It is much better to do a little bit every day, or every other day which is what I try to, rather than break your neck in the gym.

Although I have tried to exercise two or three times a week since my mid-twenties, I must confess that I am only human, and have sometimes gone for as much as a month without doing even a side bend. This usually happens either when I'm filming, travelling or working extremely hard. When that happens I *definitely* become bigger around my waist and hips, even though my actual weight has stayed more or less the same. Then I grit my teeth and throw myself back into my exercise routine with a vengeance. It usually takes about a month for me to get back to the way I want to look, and I curse myself constantly for being so lazy. Because my body is *programmed* now to respond to exercise, I'm lucky in that I can get into shape fast. Even if I'm not in the mood, I will force myself to do sit-ups while watching TV. I'm not keen on jogging or aerobics or even going to the gym. I prefer either swimming or doing the exercises I have illustrated here.

Several years ago, the *Journal of the American Medical Association* did a study which proved that 'large numbers of Americans are dying just from sitting on their behinds'! Interviewing relations of recently deceased men about their lifestyle, the AMA found that those men

MY SECRETS

who exercised regularly throughout their life lived years longer than those who had stopped exercising beyond their twenties. Another group of American interviewers contacted and surveyed a hundred people between the ages of forty-five and eighty-five who had been exercising regularly. They found that this group of people had not lost the amount of inches in height that average people do as they get older. After the age of forty-five the average person loses about half an inch in height *each decade*, but the group of a hundred exercisers had lost less than *half* that much. They also had less body fat, better heart and lung function and much better muscle tone. Their bodies were younger and stronger, their physiology was functioning extremely well, and they maintained their bodies better.

What most people don't realise is that a great part of what we think of as degeneration from age, is actually a result of not actually *using* our bodies. We are so much more sedentary than our ancestors. We drive instead of walk, go up in lifts rather than climb stairs. It's a shocking fact but if you spend twenty-four hours being inactive because of illness, flu or just plain laziness, your muscle tissue begins to deteriorate immediately. If you go a year without exercise, fifty per cent of the benefits that you gained from exercising *all your life* will be gone.

If you start exercising between the age of thirty and forty religiously for three and a half hours a week, your body can remain *virtually the same* until you are well into your sixties. Surely it's worth it then? I often get out of bed, and while I'm still in my pyjamas I do ten or fifteen minutes exercise. You shouldn't feel that you always have to be in a leotard, proper shoes and exercise gear. It is better to do a bit of exercise than none, so start today.

But an exercise programme does not have to be *intimidating*. You don't have to be a fitness freak to be fit. I will demonstrate in the following pages the best exercises for toning; increasing muscle power; and maximum suppleness.

To sum up, the benefits of exercise are enormous, but on the whole exercise alone will not make you lose weight; it will only work in combination with my advice on eating properly.

Here are some exercises which I think are beneficial to everybody.

MY SECRETS

Stretching Exercises

ARM & SIDE STRETCH

·EXERCISE 1·

Feet apart – arms above head. Hands together. Left arm over right wrist. Pull the arm up.

(Three times on each side)

NECK STRETCH

·EXERCISE 2·

Feet apart – hands at side. Bend head ear to shoulder.

(Four times to the left side – four times to right)

WAIST

·EXERCISE 3·

Feet apart. One hand on hip. Other hand stretching to ceiling. Bend from the waist pulling right arm up. (Note: it is essential to keep other hand on hip to protect the back.)

(Four times on each side)

HIP ROLL

·EXERCISE 4·

This is hard to demonstrate. Feet apart – hands on hip. Rotate hips as though you are stirring a pot of soup.

(Four times on each side)

Same exercise in the other direction.

MY SECRETS

6

LEG HAMSTRING LUNGE

· EXERCISE 5 ·
Feet apart. Right leg bent.
Left heel on the floor.
Head up – both heels stay on
the floor. Lunge forward with
the right knee. Alternate
side to side four times.

· EXERCISE 6 ·
Breathe in. Breathe out.
Hands on hip. You are now
ready for exercising.

M Y S E C R E T S

Arm Work

1A

1B

1C

LATERAL MUSCLE (LOWER SHOULDER BLADE) STRENGTHENING

·EXERCISE 1·

1A Feet together. Take your weights in each hand. (If you do not have weights use bottle of water or a soup can.) Arms over head. Pull down as though you are pulling a pulley.

1B Halfway with the exercise.

IC Judy shows me how to do it.

BICEPS

· E X E R C I S E   2 ·

Feet together. One hand on hip holding waist. Other hand flexed. Bend and stretch arm paying attention to the isolation of the bicep muscle.

(Three sets of eight for each arm)

TRICEPS

· E X E R C I S E   3 ·

Left leg in front. Straighten and bend the back arm, isolating the triceps.

(Three sets of eight for each arm)

PUSH-UPS

· E X E R C I S E   4 ·

With your body prone and extended, put your hands flat on the floor with your weight supported on your knees and your ankles crossed and raised off the ground. Push your body up, straightening your arms to full extension, then lower your body slowly and return to the starting position. Try to repeat eight times. As you progress, try three sets of eight.

M Y   S E C R E T S

Abdominal Exercises (Stomach)

SIT UPS

· E X E R C I S E 1 ·

Lie on the floor – legs on small stool or box. Arms behind head. Buttocks tight. Stomach scooped and held in. Raise shoulders and head from floor and back again ten times. Do not let head and shoulders drop back onto the floor.

(Three sets of ten)

ABDOMINAL STRENGTHENING

· E X E R C I S E 2 ·

Lie flat on your back with your arms behind your raised head. Bring one knee at a time up into the body. Judy acts as resistance while I am doing these rather difficult sit-ups.

(Three sets of ten)

STRENGTHENING AND TONING WAIST

· E X E R C I S E 3 ·

Lie flat on your back, hands behind head, feet resting on a stool. Raise the left shoulder to the right knee, and then the right shoulder to the left one.

(Three sets of ten)

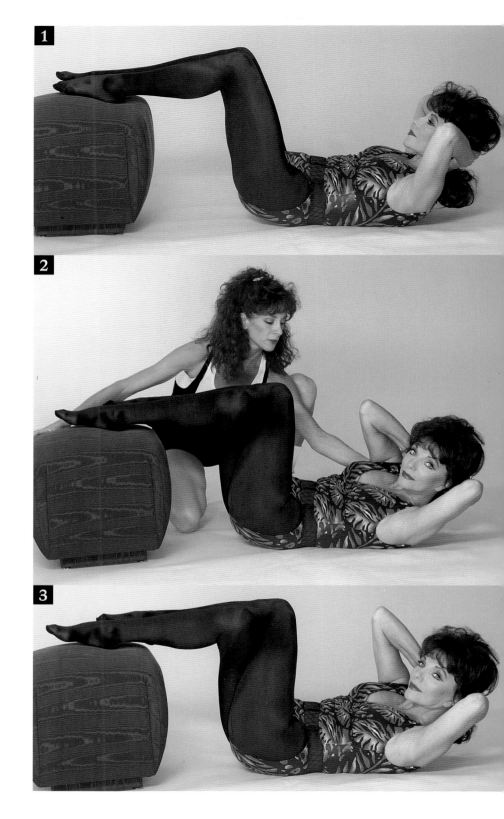

MY SECRETS

Leg and Stomach Strengthening and Toning

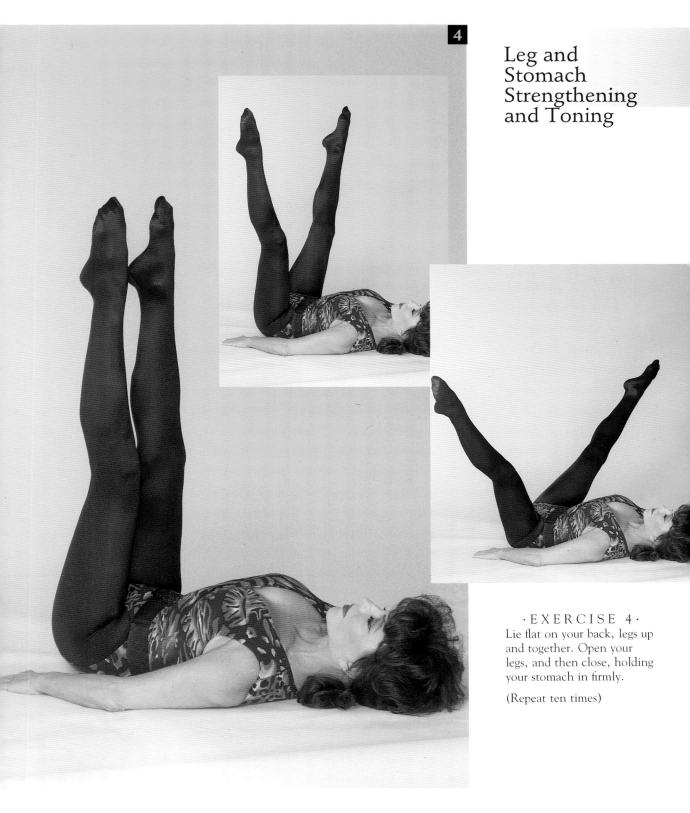

· EXERCISE 4 ·

Lie flat on your back, legs up and together. Open your legs, and then close, holding your stomach in firmly.

(Repeat ten times)

MY SECRETS

Legs

SIDE THIGH STRENGTHENING

·EXERCISE 1A·

Lie on your side supporting yourself with both hands in front of you. With one leg stretched, raise and lower the other leg. Repeat ten times. Then do it in reverse on the other side. Do three sets.

ADVANCED SIDE THIGH STRENGTHENING

·EXERCISE 1B·

Lie on your side with your weight balanced on one hand. With your right hand on your right leg, lift the leg as high as possible to its maximum extent. Do three sets of eight.

VARIATION

·EXERCISE 1C·

As above, but raise the right leg and the right arm to their fullest extent in parallel, and lower in parallel. Do three sets of eight.

INNER THIGH STRENGTHENING

· E X E R C I S E   2 A ·

Lie on side – right leg over left. Weight on left arm. Lift and lower left leg. Repeat other side.

(Three sets of ten)

2B You deserve a break. Take ten seconds for relaxation!

MY SECRETS

Buttocks

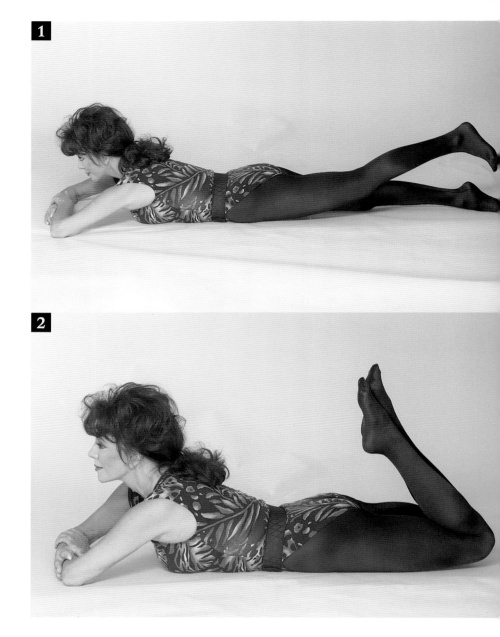

· E X E R C I S E 1 ·
Lie on your stomach with
your hips flat on the floor,
arms crossed and head
resting on your arms.
Squeeze the buttocks, and
raise your left leg ten times
with your foot flexed, then
your right leg ten times.

· E X E R C I S E 2 ·
Lie flat on your stomach, legs
bent and toes pointed, feet
and knees together. Squeeze
your buttocks and knees
together.

(Three sets of ten)

Stretches

· EXERCISE 1A ·
Sit with your left leg bent
and your right leg extended,
toes pointed. Stretch the
right leg, and pull your body
upright as much as possible.

· EXERCISE 1B ·
With one hand on your hip
and the other over your
head, bend your upper body
over the outstretched leg,
then return to the upright
position. Do three times
each side.

· EXERCISE 1C ·
My exhibition pose. This is a
version of the splits, which
completely stretches the
inner thigh. This is how I
finish my own exercise
workout, but I don't
recommend it for everybody!

Final Stretch

·EXERCISE 1·

Legs apart and hands on the floor. Lunge with your left leg keeping the right one straight; then do it in reverse, lunging with the right leg and keeping the left leg straight. Keep your back straight and parallel to the floor.

·EXERCISE 2·

Stand with your feet apart. Bend from your waist and put your hands flat on the floor. Some people cannot get their hands on to the floor, but get down as low as you can.

YOGA STRETCH

·EXERCISE 3·

Sit on the floor cross-legged. Put your hands on your knees. Rock from side to side on your buttocks. Then raise your hands above your head, hold your stomach in, and press your palms together for a count of five. Then release.

·EXERCISE 4·

Finished and feeling very pleased with myself!

MY SECRETS

CHAPTER NINE

Skin Deep

ALL ABOUT THE OUTER YOU

FACE FACTS

THERE **IS NO** question that *nothing* and *no-one* can look good without care and maintenance, but that does not necessarily mean it has to be a boring chore. I have a friend who sighs, 'Oh, I'm so busy, that I don't even have time to put moisturiser on my face.' Why doesn't she put it on straight after she cleans her teeth, I ask her. Moisturising is the simplest thing in the world, and the most necessary form of maintenance for your skin. In fact it's beauty therapy number one. I told Sue Lawley on *Desert Island Discs* that moisturiser was the one luxury that I couldn't be without. My mother started me using moisturiser in my early teens, before it was considered necessary, and I've been using it ever since, and I started my daughters on it at the same age.

As far as the nightly maintenance of the skin is concerned my routine is simple. I remove make-up with a good make-up remover. (I happen to like Nivea because it's extremely effective.) I put some toner on a piece of cotton wool and take off the residue of dirt and make-up, then I apply my nightly moisturiser. If I found myself somewhere without my moisturiser, I would put on some Vaseline. If I didn't have Vaseline I'd use olive oil or even coconut oil. On many occasions I have read letters from women in magazines and newspapers saying, 'Well of course with all her money it's easy for Joan Collins, isn't it?' But it *really* doesn't take much money or time to take care of yourself. There are, of course, skin creams on the market that are extremely expensive and I, like many other people, have been conned into buying these exotic potions and lotions. To be perfectly frank I have never

MY SECRETS

seen them do anything different to my skin than Vaseline, Nivea, or any of the cheaper cold creams. The same goes for make-up. You can buy wonderful cosmetics inexpensively at Boots, Marks & Spencer and other chain stores, but you can also buy extortionately expensive make-up in those hallowed marbled make-up halls in Harvey Nichols and Harrods.

Everybody is born with flawless skin but, starting from puberty, as we age our skin changes dramatically. The effects of sun and heredity start to show by the end of the teens. In general our skin is what people judge our age by, and it can make us look much older or much younger than we really are. Why is it that some forty-five-year-old women have smooth firm skin, while others can be rough and saggy? The answer is in how well you take care of it. Even a bad night's sleep can change how your skin looks. Illness, smoking, bad dietary habits, and using the wrong skin products can do untold damage to the skin.

So what is beautiful skin? Basically the surface is soft, firm and resilient, with small pores, and a slightly rosy glow that comes from proper blood circulation. With healthy skin any spot or blemish should heal fast because the skin is nourished, and the cell layer underneath the surface is always multiplying. It's the *underlying* tissues of the skin that make it look good.

There are essentially four stages of skin in a woman's life:

TEENS TO MID-TWENTIES: skin is taut, and there's not a wrinkle or a sag to be seen. It has an even colour and no broken blood vessels. The oil glands are functioning at their peak capacity (which is why so many adolescents get clogged pores and acne).

This very young skin needs little attention, except for scrupulous cleansing which can be done with a mild soap. A light moisturiser should be started in the teens unless the skin is very oily in which case it is not necessary.

TWENTY-FIVE TO THIRTY: skin is at its absolute peak in this period. It should be smooth and firm, with good elasticity. Sadly, although the skin may look perfect on the outside, underneath it is starting to change. If your skin is oily, your pores will be more noticeable now; or if your skin has a tendency to be dry it will now start

to become drier. In the late twenties and early thirties, the first dreaded
laughter lines begin to show up around the eyes. Because the area
around the eyes is so thin, these tiny lines are the first to show up.
Although you may not realise it, your skin is starting to thin all over.
Since these are the years in which most women become pregnant,
certain hormonal changes will be reflected in the skin. Blemishes and
discoloration can also be expected at this stage.

THIRTIES TO FORTIES: this is when deterioration in all
the skin (but particularly the skin on the face) really starts to
accelerate, unless you have been taking excellent care of it. Since
there's a huge decline in the oil production of the skin, and some
glands stop functioning, natural moisture is no longer present in most
skins. The skin becomes dry and flaky, and needs to be constantly
moisturised. As the skin is much thinner now, all kinds of
broken veins, wrinkles, freckles and marks appear. This is also
the time when all the coffee, tea, alcohol and cigarettes you
have had during your life will show up in the form of wrinkles!
There are now many more wrinkles around the eyes and
forehead, and the whole face starts to look slightly droopy.
The pores look larger. The moisture in the skin has been
depleted quite a bit, because the activity of the oil glands has
dried up, so the skin becomes more alkaline which makes it
drier, and it sometimes feels irritated, and itchy.

Because the connective tissue and collagen beneath the
skin is becoming weaker, and the face is becoming less
resilient, it is better not to have any strong facial massages.
Many women, as their skin starts to age, believe that having
firm massages will improve it. That is not true. Massage only
separates the skin from the connective tissue underneath, and can do
more damage. Mild massage however can be beneficial.

There are of course many women of this age who do not have
these kinds of skin problems, but over ninety per cent of these are
women who have taken great care of their skin all their lives. Even if
you have not been careful all your life and haven't followed any beauty
procedures it's never too late to start.

MY SECRETS

FIFTY PLUS: if you have been taking care of your skin from your late teens there is no reason now not to still have very good skin. There are plenty of examples today of women over fifty with great skin. But there is no question that once you are past fifty the skin is much more delicate than it used to be, so it needs very careful handling. Although the oil glands aren't functioning as well, it is still possible to get blemishes, because with the pores shrinking, cells will clog the pores, and sometimes spots form blackheads or whiteheads.

The epidermis, or outer layer of the skin, has thickened, while the dermis, and the subcutaneous tissue, or the inner layer, has become thinner. All the connective tissues, including collagen and elastin are weak and thinner, and no longer support the skin as well as they did. Now sagging eyelids, crêpy throat and neck, and heavy wrinkles between nose and mouth become more evident. More hair grows on the face, and the lips can become thinner as the gums recede and deteriorate. Blue veins can show through, and often the skin has a greyish pallor.

So, to prevent all this, here are some of my skin-saving tips:

SLEEP is absolutely *essential* for a good skin. You can see, even when you're young, what lack of sleep can do to your skin. Young people can always recoup their energy, but if you miss hours of sleep at forty you're going to see it showing up in your skin. Sleep is essential, because the nutrients that help new skin cells to form cannot be properly assimilated without it, neither can oxygen be brought to the skin properly. If you really have problems sleeping one of the reasons may be because you haven't taken enough calcium during the day. If the calcium level falls, your nerves become tense, and your muscles contract. The older you get the more calcium you need, because the ability to absorb it diminishes. That old staple a glass of warm milk can help, as milk contains lots of calcium. Another thing I have found that helps me sleep, is to eat half a mashed banana mixed with a little yoghurt and honey.

STOP FROWNING, making faces or twisting your face into exaggerated expressions. The actress, Linda Darnell, who was famous for her impassive look on the screen (you may have seen her in *Forever*

MY SECRETS

Amber) was a firm believer in moving her facial muscles as little as possible. Unfortunately this didn't do a lot for her acting, but when she died tragically in her forties she was renowned for her amazingly unlined skin, thanks to hardly moving it. Well I don't advocate *that*, but I do think that we should frown a little less and smile a little more.

L O V E Being in love is without a doubt one of the best beauty treatments that there is. Sexual love is great therapy for your skin because sexual excitement brings an excellent supply of oxygen and blood to it.

F R E S H   A I R Being in an office, shop or factory with constant heating or air-conditioning day after day makes your skin dingy and dried out. Walking in the open air is one of the best things you can do for your skin. However it is *essential* to protect yourself with moisturiser, sun block, and, if necessary, make-up.

S K I N   T I P S If your skin is irritated, whether from the cold weather, or too much air-conditioning, use milk as a cleanser and toner. Wash the face thoroughly with milk and then rinse it all with warm water. You could also try a luxurious milk bath à la Cleopatra. Empty half a box of dried milk into the bath tub and soak in it for half an hour. You'll feel really refreshed and re-energised.

If the skin around your eyes is very dry, pierce a vitamin E capsule, and pat the oil around your lids in the morning, and at night. Leave it on while you shower or bath, as the steam helps the oil penetrate the skin.

Never leave make-up on overnight; once you've done it once and you still look all right the next day, you'll think you can do it again. Bad habits catch up on us much too fast, so remove that make-up *every single night*.

Always moisturise your face and body when your skin is *damp*; that allows it to penetrate more thoroughly.

Always wear sunblock, even in the winter.

If you're feeling tired after work and are going to a party or dinner and your eyes look puffy, lie down in a darkened room for five minutes and put a teabag moistened with cold water over each eye. This will

If a man is old only in years then he is indeed old in vain.

(THE DHAMMAPADA)

M Y   S E C R E T S

seriously reduce any puffiness around the eyes. (Make sure you wipe the tannin off your skin though as it could negate the effect and make you look like a panda!)

Drink plenty of water for beautiful skin.

Avoid excessive heat and excessive cold. Since nowadays most modern work-places turn up the heat when it's cold, and vice versa, our skin is constantly having to suffer these extremes of temperature. I myself rarely turn on either heating or air conditioning.

I am one of many who believe that overly strenuous exercise and sport are bad for women – they wear out your body and skin damage and weakening can occur in the connective tissue and collagen of women when they are doing aerobics, jogging too energetically, or jumping. Every time you step or jump the breasts, buttocks and chin, which are not supported, are hurled downward creating loose chins, sagging breasts and flabby bottoms.

If you put anything on your skin that makes it feel itchy, tight, uncomfortable or in any way strange and different, throw that product away whatever it is. It may mean that your skin is allergic to it, and although we do not know why, there seem to be many more allergies towards certain products in recent years. I believe it is because our immune systems are fighting the toxins and poisons in the environment. Therefore if a product, whether a cream or a cosmetic, has some sort of substance in it that does not agree with you, discontinue it. On the left is a list of some of the ingredients that are known to have been irritating to some skins.

To slow down the ageing of your face you must speed up its cell production. In youth, new skin cells move rapidly to the surface, and flake away equally rapidly when they die to make room for new cells. However, as we age, the old dead cells linger on the skin's surface. They don't reflect the light and are dull and rough. Removing them helps the skin to look and become younger because it has to work harder to produce the new cells.

Make sure you regularly get rid of dead cells. This can be done with either a peel-off mask or a clay mask. I find the best way, however, if your skin is not too delicate, is to rub the cells away. For this you need cleansing grains, an abrasive sponge, and a natural animal hair brush.

INGREDIENTS KNOWN TO BE HARMFUL TO SOME SKINS

Acacia	Hydroquinone
Alizarin	Karaya gum
Alkaline earth sulphides	Lanolin
	Lead
Alum	Lycopodium
Aluminium sulphate	Phenol
	Resorcinol
Arrowroot	Rice starch
Boric acid	Salicylic acid
Cocoa butter	Wheat starch
Corn starch	Zinc chloride
Formaldehyde	Zinc sulphate
Gum Arabic	
Gum Tragacanth	

OILS

Almond	Lemon
Bay	Linseed
Cottonseed	Orange
Coriander	Wintergreen
Eucalyptus	

MY SECRETS

Another excellent way that I slough off dead skin, is sugar abrasion, which is very inexpensive, effective and easy to do.

Remove your make-up, and if you wish wash your face (I don't like to use soap on my skin because it is dry but if you do, choose a very low alkaline soap). Smooth olive oil all over your face. Then apply either brown or white granulated sugar dotting it on your cheeks, forehead, chin, nose and throat, omitting the area under the eyes. You will find the sugar sticks to the oil on the skin. Using your fingertips, gently rub the sugar across the skin's surface. Don't press, as the granules themselves will loosen the dead skin cells. Use small circular motions, and try *not* to stretch the skin. The sugar will dissolve in about thirty seconds. Then with warm water wash away the oil, sugar, and the dead cells. Rinse several times to get rid of any residue. If you use the abrasion technique before a facial mask or other treatment, you will find it much more effective. I suggest doing this every day for about three weeks, and then two or three times a week.

After any form of abrasion the one thing you should not do for a few days is to put your face in the sun. New cells are much more vulnerable to ultra violet rays, so you *must* protect them. The abrasion has unblocked pores, so the natural oils are flowing more freely, but it is essential to use a moisturiser.

HOME IMPROVEMENTS

I'm not an advocate of plastic surgery because I've seen too many mistakes and disasters on the faces of women *and* men in America. I have however seen people who look much better after a 'make-over'; but they looked completely different. I don't think that the average woman wants to go around with the world knowing that she's been so obviously 'done'. Of course there are many cases where the surgery has been satisfactory, in which case you should look like you looked before, but better.

Eye surgery means having the knife close to the eyelids, and as this is the most dangerous and delicate part of plastic surgery I would not recommend it. I have seen several people who have had their under eye bags removed, but in most cases the bags returned within two or three years.

I had dinner with a friend recently who had a face-lift several

years ago, but in the harsh light of the restaurant, the left side of her face seemed to be twisted and drooping. It was not a pretty sight and I thought she would have done better to have left her face alone, and lost some weight instead. However, for the future I shall reserve the right to have plastic surgery should I feel the need arise.

There are too many unqualified plastic surgeons around, so if you want to find one, make sure he's a reputable one, and get a second opinion.

LIPOSUCTION

My favourite remark about this procedure, which many people in California swear by, was said of a famous actress, 'She's had so much liposuction she looks Hoovered!'

This is another cosmetic make-over operation which I don't recommend. It is a form of instant dieting, which sucks the fat from your body with a small vacuum device. All fat cells are supposedly removed, never to return, but I know some fat people who have had it done and you could've fooled me! Small holes are of course left on the skin's surface, so wearing a bathing suit is probably not a good idea for some time afterwards. The scars will always be there, not to mention some rather saggy skin, unless you've toned up radically.

Tom Arnold, the husband of Roseanne Barr, went in for liposuction on his 'love handles' while I was rehearsing a show with Roseanne last year. When he returned four days later he *did* look thinner but he said he was in a lot of pain. He did a stand-up comedy routine about his operation which had us all in stitches. I hope it didn't split his!

SILICONE INJECTIONS

Silicone has fallen into disfavour recently, particularly in breast implants, where there have been reports of some carcinomas occurring, and some women have had bad reactions. Surgeons are now substituting saline implants, which are thought to be much safer. Breast implants are a boon for women who have had a mastectomy; if I had one I wouldn't hesitate to have implants myself. Again the right surgeon with proper credentials is a must. *Know* your doctor and talk to him at length about the procedure. In any case on the subject of

We're Regency Rakes
And each of us makes
A personal issue
Of adipose tissue.

(NOEL COWARD)

mastectomy or indeed ANY major operation which involves the removal of any part of your body it is vital to have at least *two* other doctors' opinions.

COLLAGEN INJECTIONS

Collagen can be injected into the cheeks and lips, or anywhere the skin needs plumping up. It has become extremely popular with movie actresses and socialities, who favour the 'pouty' look. The down side is that it doesn't last, and to keep that pout, the collagen injections have to be continued regularly. It is also apparently extremely painful while being injected into the skin.

PEELING OR DERMABRASION

This can be extremely dangerous unless done by a qualified practitioner; even then it is not 100 per cent safe.

The top layer of skin, and all the imperfections it contains, is peeled off, removing pockmarks, some surface wrinkles, discoloration and freckles, skin cancers, but it takes a very long time before the skin is back to normal again.

I have not tried dermabrasion as I have sensitive skin, but a friend, who also has a very delicate fair skin, had a radical dermabrasion several years ago, and the operation removed more than the surface layers: her tender skin was ruined and she couldn't be seen publicly for two years! I'm glad to say that eventually she recovered but it was a terrible shock both to her and her friends.

There are many different types of gentle dermabrasion. Some dermatologists do it with a high-speed rotating wire brush; after the application of a numbing agent to anaesthetise the area, the top layer is brushed and peeled off. It takes about half an hour. Then for two weeks you have to stay at home and avoid any contact with sun, fresh air or daylight. But at the end of this procedure, if you survive all this, claim the advocates, you should be left with a gorgeous new skin.

LIGHT EPIDERMABRASION (The Buf-Puf) Using a cleansing, slightly abrasive, plastic sponge you gently remove the top layer of dead skin cells. I would advise it only for tougher, more oily skins, but you could experiment extremely carefully for the first couple

MY SECRETS

of times and see how your skin reacts. It is, however, excellent for removing skin on the elbows and knees.

S L E N D E R T O N E   This machine is guaranteed to remove inches from your body and it worked for me!

I first tried Slendertone several months after my first baby was born when I still couldn't get into my dresses. After a course of four or five treatments I was thrilled to see my body return to its normal size.

You lie on a table, and the operator attaches various straps to the parts of the body where you need to lose weight, e.g. upper arms, stomach, thighs, waist, etc. (They can basically be attached anywhere on your body except for face and bosom.)

The straps are then attached to a rather alarming looking machine which peeps and squeaks, and has many red and yellow lights flashing on it. This sends electric impulses to the wrapped body which make the muscles automatically contract. It's rather like doing lots of repetitions of a particular exercise, but lying down and reading a book or watching the television while you're working out. It's very time-consuming (an hour and a half) but eventually worth the effort if you want to lose on a particular area and lose fast.

There are several Slendertone salons in Britain, but you can also buy the machine yourself for home use, although it is expensive.

HANDS IN HAND

Because the skin on the back of the hands is so thin a lack of care shows up faster than any other part of our body. We also lose fat cells from the back of our hands faster than any other part of our body. By the age of forty the ghastly fact is that most women only have *half* as many fat cells in their hands as men! Which is why the hands of a man of forty in general look younger than a woman's of the same age. The maintenance of hands is relatively simple. Wear rubber gloves or disposable plastic peel-off gloves whenever you put your hands in water for any length of time for washing up, or doing laundry. The same rule applies to hands as to face. MOISTURISE!! Keep a bottle of hand and body lotion in your bathroom and next to the sink in your kitchen. Massage it in up to your elbows whenever you wash your hands and after bathing.

M Y   S E C R E T S

I agree that the maintenance of toe nails and finger nails can be time consuming, particularly if you have professional manicures and pedicures, which I do. But it's relatively easy to maintain nails and toe nails, with a weekly do-it-yourself session.

SMILE, PLEASE!

It is, of course, extremely important to take care of your teeth, but what many people seem to ignore is their gums which are equally, if not more important. I have a wonderful dentist in London who has given me some excellent tips for taking care of teeth and gums.

Gum disease is the loss of gum and bone, which, if not treated properly, is a progressive and irreversible disease. The expression 'long in the tooth' refers to the fact that as we age the gums shrink and therefore the teeth become more prominent and appear bigger. Gum disease is quite serious and needs to be kept in check by regular brushing of the gums, preferably with an electric toothbrush. This is one of the best investments for your teeth that you can buy.

I also believe strongly in fluoride toothpaste. My children, now all in their twenties always used it and today *none* of them have any cavities.

Most people brush their teeth incorrectly, using strong horizontal strokes that damage gums and don't get to the areas where plaque collects. Remember it's *in between* the teeth that we need to clean always. Hold the brush at forty-five degree angle and brush with up and down movements. Always use dental floss in addition to brushing your teeth and see your dentist as soon as any problem develops. The sooner you see him the easier the cure will be.

HAIR RAISING

Hair is probably the bane of most women's lives (it is certainly mine), and accounts for their biggest expenditure in time and money. Many people make the mistake of using the same shampoo all the time. Since

MY SECRETS

hair adjusts to the same shampoo I change my brand every three or four months, and can usually see the difference in my hair. I don't use a lot of conditioner as I think it gunges up the hair. I only condition mine about every two weeks and I wash it every two days. Trimming split ends is essential, otherwise the whole hair shaft can become split.

The worst things for hair are:

☐Hot rollers.

☐Blow-drying while hair is still wet, and pulling on it with a brush.

☐Pulling at the hair either from the roots or pulling tangles is disastrous. Since we start losing hair rapidly from the age of about thirty we need to hang on to all we've got!

☐Perming: especially for fine hair, this can be disastrous.

☐Tinting: particularly going blonde. Peroxide is a killer for the hair.

I have very fine hair, which I know how to handle. If I really want to make it look thicker I do the following: after shampooing, and while still wet, I spray setting lotion all over the hair from roots to the ends (I prefer Pantène or l'Oréal). Then I either let it dry naturally, or if I'm in a hurry, blow-dry it with my head bent over. Blow-drying from underneath, section by section gives the hair much more body. Once the layers are dry, I brush it out and wind the hair onto large mesh rollers, applying a tiny bit of setting lotion or hair-spray to each rolled section. It is much better to dry your hair naturally then. Another method is to attach a hair cap to your blow-dryer, and sit under it for fifteen minutes, by which time the hair should be dry and ready for action.

After taking out the rollers, I back-comb the roots of the hair with a very fine comb, then take each section and back-comb it again lightly. After brushing it into place, my hair has a great deal more volume. It is actually easier to give volume to fine hair than any other type, but I must admit it is a lot of work. Unfortunately with my kind of hair, it doesn't always last, but if the set starts to flop, it can be revived by bending over and gently brushing or combing from underneath.

Wigs are a boon for women with difficult

Do blondes really have more fun? Or do redheads, carrot-heads or even purple-heads?

hair, or even for women with good hair. I see no reason why anyone should have any qualms about wearing a wig occasionally. Most of the time in *Dynasty* I wore a wig; it was short and terribly easy to take care of. While Linda Evans and the others spent hours having their hair rolled, sprayed and back-combed, I spent five minutes putting on my wig, which gave me a lot more time to learn my lines! I don't wear wigs every day when I'm not working. I usually just let my hair loose with a headband on it, or I wear hats, which I love.

There are unbelievable choices of really good, inexpensive wigs today, made of Kanekolon, or Dylon. Asian hair usually made in Korea is the best. You can treat a wig quite roughly, much more roughly than your own hair. The worse it's treated the better it will actually look, more like real hair in fact. Because wigs are so cheap and they don't wear out easily, there's no reason not to have a wardrobe of them if you are so inclined.

Postiches, plaits, braids, falls are all useful things to attach to your own hair. You want to change the way you dress don't you, so why not change the way your hair looks? With hairpieces and wigs it's as simple as a, b, c! Nobody has the time to go to the hairdresser three times a week unless she is a professional model or an actress. Few women even have the time for it once a month. What you need is a quick and easy style, easy enough to do yourself, one that will always look good. The more aware you are of your hair type, the better you will be able to deal with it in terms of styling and setting. So find out what kind of hair you have, then learn to make the best of it.

Madame Tussaud's made a wax-work of me in the late 1980s. Not satisfied with her coiffure, I attempted a better style.

HAIR EXTENSIONS

Hair extensions are becoming very popular in the States. This is a secret that the super-models have known about for years. I have worn them, and have found them great for a couple of weeks although they have a tendency to get clumpy, and are quite uncomfortable to sleep in. Extensions consist of weaving real hair on to your own, near the scalp. There are several different ways of doing this, the most popular being to sew the new hair on to tiny plaits of your own hair close to your scalp. It can also be done by bonding, in which the false hair is stuck on to a swatch of your own hair with a machine, or on to the scalp with glue.

.   .   .

MY SECRETS

Absolutely everyone seems dissatisfied with her natural hair – but you have to accept your hair for what it is, understand its limitations and never try to force it into a style that won't work. If your hair looks good, you feel good.

Here are some of my secrets for beautiful hair:

□ If you must back-comb, take great care when you brush out, as it is far too easy to snap off precious strands.

□ *Never* use a metal comb. Natural bone or strong plastics are the best. The same goes for hair brushes: boars' bristle brushes are good.

□ Cut your own split ends regularly. Make sure your hair is clean and wet, and that your scissors are very sharp and haven't been cutting up things in the kitchen.

□ When using a hand dryer don't keep the heat on one section for longer than a couple of minutes.

□ *Never* use rollers with plastic or metal spikes. They can destroy your hair as can going under a hot hair dryer for a long time.

□ The best way to set fine hair is to roll the clean hair up dry, and spray it with hair spray. Leave in for fifteen minutes and when you take it out you'll have more bounce than ever.

□ If you have too much electricity in your hair pass an anti-static sheet over it, the kind you put in the washing machine.

Take care of any small patches of grey with a tint and a small toothbrush.

If you want to colour your hair at home it is quite simple as long as you use rubber gloves and follow the instructions to the letter.

If you do get tint on your skin or hairline, a good remover is to mix cigarette ash with a little water and rub gently. The stain will come right out.

BREAST CARE

There is no woman I know who is satisfied with her bosom, but there are many things you can do to improve the look of it. *Always* wear a bra, particularly when you exercise, and make sure it fits properly. Make sure you get measured properly so that you know what your cup size is and always pull the straps up enough to give a good shape. I prefer bras not covered in lace which shows through your clothes and

---

MY FAVOURITE HAIR PRODUCTS

PANTÈNE SETTING LOTION AND AMAMI SETTING LOTION.

VIDAL SASSOON SHAMPOO AND CONDITIONER.

AUSSIE SPRUNCH SPRAY (made in the USA but available in certain places in the UK).

MASON PEARSON PURE BEAR BRISTLE BRUSHES.

ARIUS – HARD RUBBER COMB.

JOHNSON & JOHNSON – 'NO MORE TANGLES' DETANGLER.

KMS TRILOGY.

HAIR CARE DETANGLE SPRAY AND WIRE & MESH ROLLERS – *without* the brushes inside.

MY SECRETS

detracts from the outfit.

The Gossard Wonder Bra could be the answer if you aren't well-endowed. It has a little padding on the bra's underside which thrusts the breasts upwards, and makes a 32B look like a 34C. You can also do cosmetic contouring by stroking a brownish pink blusher in the hollow between the breasts when you are wearing a low-cut dress. Blend it carefully so that it looks completely natural. If you are wearing a backless dress and don't have the right bra, do what all the models do: take transparent first-aid tape and tape 'em up! Start underneath the arm pit on the right hand side, run the tape *under* your breasts, and up the other side, pulling the breasts together as you tape. The effect although temporary is quite incredible, and is used by many models and actresses.

To make a small bosom look bigger without using a push-up bra, wear an 'Empire Line' dress, made popular by the Empress Josephine, which is terribly flattering and attractive.

To make a large bosom look smaller, *never* wear tight sweaters, dresses, or high necks. A V-neck blouse or shirt always detracts from a too big bosom. A shirt with a yoke at the back can make a bosom look less big. Loose dresses can only make you look worse. If you have any kind of a waist accentuate it with a belt. That will make a big chest look better.

Always put body lotion on your breasts as well. Since they have no muscle, it is important to do exercises to maintain them. The best bust-firming exercise I have found is to stand with feet apart, clasp hands together in front of your bust, and raise elbows to the sides. Press your palms together as hard as you can. Release. Repeat twelve times. Also cold water splashed on the breasts after a bath or shower helps keep them firm. Always check for any change in your breasts and if you find *any* kind of lump, go to your doctor *immediately*. Even if it is benign, (and these little lumps and bumps usually are) *every day* is vital. Breast cancer if caught early enough is often curable. And if you are over forty, or have a history of cancer in your family you should have a mammogram *every year*.

I still prefer myself
with my own colour hair.
London 1992.

TO TAN OR NOT TO TAN

Tanning your skin is without any shadow of a doubt the worst thing you

MY SECRETS

can do to it. But nothing I can say is going to stop those of you who want to carry on doing it. Unfortunately nothing makes us look better than a rich golden tan. There's no question that in the summer a lightly tanned body looks better than a pink, white, or freckled one. If your eyes are pale it accentuates them until they look like semi-precious stones – if they're dark, even better. There is a glow and a glamour to a tan no make-up or beauty product can give. Teeth look whiter, eyes brighter, the whole skin seems to glow. The trouble is that if you have tanned yourself for years you will find that your skin will never get back that translucent child-like quality it had before.

In Britain we never seem to get enough sunlight; as soon as the sun comes out the parks are littered with milk-white bodies soaking up

In the 1960s I still tanned every part of myself, including my face, without worrying about sun damage.

those glorious rays. A certain amount of sunlight does make us feel good but we don't have to *soak* in it. We can just walk in the sun (with block on, of course!) to let it do us good. I find all the elements of weather, other than freezing bitter cold or blistering heat, are energy enhancers. I always feel refreshed after a long brisk walk with the wind whipping my hair and a little gentle rain. I never allow the sun to touch my face directly, but I still tan my body, because I adore the feeling of the sun on my skin. I wear sunblock on my face, and end up with a brown body and a white face. But I much prefer that to having a wrinkled face, and I never lie in the sun too long. I see women in St Tropez who go to the beach at 10 a.m. and stay there baking until 7 p.m. every day for two months which is skin-suicide. I realize from my own sunbathing activities that the skin on my face is much better than the skin on my body, and this is only the aesthetic consideration – think of the danger of skin cancer.

According to Dr Oswald Morton, a doctor at the Windsor Health Care, which manufactures Uvistat, between the ages of twenty and seventy the skin ages very little. The unexposed skin on the buttocks of a seventy-year-old is not that much different from that of a twenty-year-old. The visible changes in the skin especially on the face and hands are almost *entirely* due to sun exposure and not to age.

Have you seen any photographs of Brigitte Bardot lately? If you're over forty you'll know what I mean. Her face is a testament to the

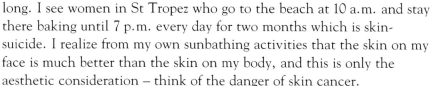

MY SECRETS

ravages of one of Western woman's favourite pursuits – sunbathing. The curse of modern civilisation and certainly the curse of those who want to retain their looks.

I remember seeing B.B., as she was called, in the mid-fifties in the bar of the Hotel de la Ville in Rome. I was the youngest in a group of seven or eight young actors who would meet for a drink and a gossip at the end of the day's filming. I was also, owing to my youth and looks, the centre of attention – until B.B. walked in. Every man there turned his head as if by magic to follow this blonde vision. And vision she was. Eat your heart out Claudia Schiffer, who is often compared to Bardot. There is *no* comparison. B.B. was infinitely more beautiful and alluring. Hand-span waist, tall, fabulous cleavage, blonde tumbling hair to kill for, and a gorgeous deeply tanned skin.

The men oohed and aahed, the women turned various shades of green, and I, who was playing an Egyptian Princess in *Land of the Pharaohs*, vowed to work even harder at my tan.

Shortly after seeing B.B. in Rome, I went under contract to Twentieth Century Fox in Hollywood and continued happily tanning my mahogany face. Cappy Badrutt, a great friend and pale-faced beauty, observed me by her pool one day, and yanked me to the swimming pool at the Beverly Hills Hotel for lunch.

'Do you see those women?' she asked, pointing to some leathery crocodile-faced creatures lounging by the pool. 'Do you want to look like them when you're thirty or forty?'

'God no!' I gasped. 'Their skin looks like saddle hide.'

'That's because of the sun!' said Cappy, bluntly. 'Not now when you're twenty-two – maybe not even thirty-two because you're dark, but I guarantee you by the time you're forty your skin will be *ruined* unless you keep your face out of the sun and take care of it properly.'

She scared me so much that I took her advice and kept my face out of the sun.

Compare the back of your hand to the skin on the inside of your upper arm. See the difference? That is not age, it's sun damage; but it doesn't matter what we are told, those alluring rays still beckon us. One of the insidious things about sunbathing is that the effects will not show up on your skin for fifteen or twenty-five years. When a twenty-five or thirty-five-year-old smugly says to you, 'Well, *I* sunbathe and it hasn't

hurt my skin at all,' you can tell her, that it may not show now, but wait until she's forty-five. Sun damage shows up with horrifying rapidity. It will probably creep up on you during the winter, when you are not taking that much notice of the skin on your body. Then, come early summer, just in time to don the bikini, all the signs of accumulated sun damage will suddenly start to show: wrinkled, mottled skin, big ugly freckles, white marks.

But nothing beats lying in the sun. I have worshipped it all my life and in fact I still do. I am simply not about to give up something I adore because it's harmful. But never *ever* on my face!!

I'm sure that sunblocks give a certain amount of protection, but a foundation and powder (on your face *over* a sun block) act like a net curtain over windows. They totally prevent the sun from ruining the furniture!

My own rules for tanning safely are:

□ Apply sun-care preparations with a generous hand often as the skin's natural bacteria, perspiration, and swimming can all erode the effectiveness of any product. Even if it claims to be water resistant, very few are completely sun-blocked, so keep putting that stuff on.

□ Treat your skin gently. Build up a tolerance to the sun from day one. If you're fair skinned don't stay in it more than twenty minutes, the first day, if you're medium skinned, thirty minutes, and if you're dark-skinned, half an hour. Day two you can take ten or fifteen minutes more with each skin group. Day three, another fifteen minutes, and on day four you could be up to one hour a day safe tanning.

□ *Never* tan in the hours between 10 a.m. and 4 p.m. That's the time to laze under an umbrella with the new best-seller. That is when the sun's ultra-violet rays are their most potent and lethal. Dermatologists say that that is the time when the major damage is done to our skin.

□ Always use a sun block even when just going shopping. The sun's rays can penetrate even through dense clouds.

□ Use make-up base on your face if you want NO sun on it at all. My favourite right now is Kanebo Total Finish, with UV protection which is a base and a powder in one.

Opposite: The power of the sun has always lured me with it's fiery rays.

Now in the 1990s when I'm relaxing and tanning I always cover up my face, even if I do look like a fugitive from the French Foreign Legion. France, 1993.

□Always wear a hat or a visor, even when swimming if you don't want sun on your face.

□ The sun and sea water and chlorine ruin the hair. I always keep mine covered with a scarf or turban when I swim and if it does get wet I use plenty of conditioner afterwards.

RETIN A

Retin A renews and rebuilds the skin cells making skin look less rough and wrinkled. Most creams just hydrate the skin surface, restore lost water and puff it up, but Retin A goes deep into the skin layers, and actually stimulates new cell growth. Since its discovery a few years ago, doctors and dermatologists have hardly been able to keep up with the demand, and those who have used it find that if their skin can tolerate it (and some cannot) it definitely does make the skin look younger, smoothing out wrinkles, sun-spots and marks. It restores the skin tone, making it softer, smoother and giving it a more rosy glow. But you have to be patient, which many of us are not. It usually takes six months to show any effect at all. Cher swears by the stuff and she looks great.

Retin A must be prescribed by a doctor or dermatologist and you should not use it when pregnant or breast-feeding or when you are going to be in direct sunlight, as it can seriously inflame your face. Nine out of ten people have an adverse reaction when they first start using it.

PRE-MENSTRUAL SYNDROME

PMS is an unfortunate condition that affects millions of women, sometimes for up to ten days before the beginning of their period. Symptoms such as depression, irritability, bloating, insomnia, crying fits and various aches and pains, are their sad lot. Some women have even become suicidal. It has been used as a defence in certain murder cases! Many doctors have said, 'It's all in the mind, just get on with life. Your mothers and your grandmothers didn't have PMS, why should you?' There is still a controversy as to whether or not PMS actually exists. Certainly when I was a teenager we never discussed it, and nobody I knew ever experienced those kind of problems but then there were many things we didn't discuss, so perhaps many of my girl friends suffered in silence.

At their annual conference, The British Psychological Society

recently devoted a whole day to arguing that PMS was a *psychological* disease rather than a *physical* one. Some doctors were fiercely opposed to this idea, as were women who were PMS sufferers.

Everybody has mood swings. We are all different in small ways from one day to the next, but these mood swings are often exacerbated during certain times of the month. Perhaps more women attribute their mood swings to PMS these days.

So what can *you* do to combat PMS? There are several things. Eat less sodium and salty foods, which include all processed cheeses, canned soups and pickles. Salt contributes to water retention. Avoid cold or iced drinks, and ice-cream; they have an adverse effect on abdominal circulation and can make PMS worse, and contribute to cramps. Try to cut down all caffeine intake: tea, chocolate, colas including diet colas, and cocoa. If you *must* drink tea, take it with milk. The milk takes out the tannin which binds important minerals and prevents absorption into the digestive tract. Avoid alcohol and fat. Eat a lot of fruit and vegetables. Increase foods with a natural diuretic ingredient. Examples: watermelon (and you can eat the seeds too), artichokes, asparagus, watercress, parsley, strawberries, raw sunflower seeds, bananas, peaches, potatoes, peanuts, figs, dates and tomatoes.

Vitamin supplements should include vitamin B6, 2mg a day. This according to Dr Guy Abraham, an American specialist on this subject, is shown to alleviate most of the PMS symptoms. Vitamin B6 reduces water retention, calms nervous tension, and preserves higher blood levels of magnesium. You must take twice as much magnesium as calcium per day. A deficiency of magnesium as well as a deficiency of B6 can cause PMS.

Vitamin E can reduce the tenderness in the breasts which sometimes is associated with PMS. And last but not least take evening primrose oil, which I believe is something we should take all the time; it is rich in gamma-linoleic (GLA), one of the essential building blocks which the body needs to renew itself.

CHAPTER TEN

The Magic of Make-Up

CHANGING FACES

Having followed my instructions for how to put on the perfect make-up, I'm now camera ready.

ABEAUTY ROUTINE should be fast, relatively effortless. Most of all, it should be enjoyable and fun.

I'm a great believer in make-up. If you think that your skin is the unwitting recipient of all the pollution in the air, you'll realise that it needs protection, and make-up is the most sensible form of that. The women I know who have worn make-up all their lives have far better skin than the ones who haven't – simply because they've protected their skin.

One of the great misconceptions about make-up is that the more you plaster it on, the younger you'll look. The opposite is in fact true. A heavy base or foundation on a lined, wrinkled skin only makes those lines show up a hundred times more. (The jokes about using polyfilla are completely untrue.) But make-up, lightly and subtly applied, can make you look younger. Nowadays make-up should not look too conspicuous. The natural look is in for most women.

Experimenting with cosmetics doesn't mean spending tons of money. The best way to find out what suits you is to ask for a free make-up demonstration at a department store, determine what colours suit you best, then buy the same shades through a less expensive manufacturer.

When I was signed up at twenty-one to Twentieth Century Fox, I had ample opportunity to study the Hollywood beauty-making machine as demonstrated by the make-up and hair experts I watched at

Fox and MGM studios. I learned early in my career how to make the best of my face from some of the mistakes that were perpetrated on it. I had watched in horror as thick panstick and three-inch eyelashes were applied to my teenaged baby features during my first few films in England. In Hollywood, Whitey Snyder, the make-up man responsible for Marilyn Monroe's gorgeous visage, was assigned to me on my first film, *The Girl in the Red Velvet Swing*. For the first time a make-up expert made me up so that I didn't look like one of my great aunts in her salad days. Whitey showed me how to put a base on so thinly, blend it so delicately, and shade it so subtly that it was hard to tell the difference between cosmetics and my own skin. Whitey did a great job of making me look seventeen when in fact I was twenty-one. One day I persuaded him to let me do it myself under his guidance, and that was the beginning of a very close relationship with my face.

Since then, I have always insisted on doing my own make-up for movies and TV. Not only do I do it better than most make-up artists, but I do it faster, more professionally and, since I know my own face far better than they do, I know what's right for it and what's wrong.

SOME OF MY MAKE-UP DOS & DON'TS

When I was asked to do the cover of the American *Harper's Bazaar* for an article on 'fabulous-over-forties' they insisted that the famous make-up artist Way Bandy must make me up. 'But why?' I asked.

'Because we wanna give you a different look,' they said.

'What's wrong with my usual look?' I asked. 'It seems to work pretty well for me.'

'If you want the August cover you gotta let Way do it his way. He'll make you look fabulous.'

So I presented myself at the New York studio of super-photographer Francesco Scavullo, bright and early at nine o'clock one morning. I had expected that make-up and hair would take about two hours, and that I would be out of there by lunchtime. Wrong! Way Bandy, whom I liked, and who had stood over me for several photographic sessions previously while I had done my own face, opened up his enormous box of tricks which contained countless brushes, pots of paint and lipsticks, and proceeded to put base on my face. He blended and shaded, he shadowed and mixed, he designed a palette of

MY SECRETS

chiaroscuro for my cheeks of which Renoir would have been proud. Dark orangey red quickly became pale rosy pink. Still not satisfied, he scrubbed it all off my face and started again. After an hour and a half of having had several different masks painted on to my skin which was starting to feel uncomfortably tingly, I asked Way how much longer it would take. 'Oh, we've only just begun,' he said airily. 'As soon as I've got the base on right, I'll start on the eyes.' Inwardly I groaned as Suga, the petite Japanese hair-stylist of the moment, hot-rollered my locks. Another hour went by as Way put eye shadow on and then took it off my by now extremely sore eyes. The more he applied the different colour mauves and browns to my eyes, the smaller they started to look. After each application he stood back proudly surveying his handiwork. Finally I looked at the finished product, and saw a face I didn't recognise: orangey pink puffy cheeks, tiny rat-like eyes with old-fashioned spidery false eyelashes glued on, eyebrows plucked thin and wispy. The picture made the cover but I looked awful.

By contrast, soon after I did a cover for the *Sunday Mirror Magazine*. I went in to John Swannell's studio at three p.m. with my normal everyday make-up on. The make-up artist quickly put a few hot rollers in my hair. I applied a bit more eye make-up and lipstick slightly stronger than usual. Fifteen minutes later, I put on a great dress and sat in front of John's camera. I turned this way and that way and after forty-five minutes it was all over.

What I'm really trying to say is that generally speaking, if you have been doing your own hair and make-up for several years, are good at it, and are satisfied with the way you look, there's probably not too much other so-called experts can tell you. Except me of course!

Whatever suits *you* is today's make-up philosophy. If you like heavy lashes and pale lips, wear them if they look good on you. If brown lips, white skin and plucked eyebrows suit you – why not? The only rule today is it mustn't look overdone.

I love experimenting with different cosmetics but I always come back to the basic colours that suit my face. I know what suits me and what doesn't, and how to apply it with a minimum of fuss.

This should be the aim of every woman: to have your make-up routine down to a fine art. Streamline your make-up drawer and tools; and experiment sufficiently to know the good and the bad points of

MY SECRETS

your face well enough to accentuate or detract from them as necessary.

I believe in experimenting on my face. My dressing table is a private world of my own where I can get away from everything, even if only for a few minutes. Here is my basic make-up routine:

1. Clean with a toner and cotton wool. Toners vary a great deal, so you must find the correct one for your skin type: very dry, dry, medium, or oily. Do not scrub skin – pat it gently.

2. Apply moisturiser while face and neck are still damp from toner.

3. Dot foundation on to your face and neck, and blend. Don't forget the neck too. I mix my own foundation to suit the colour of my skin. The only time I go more than one shade darker than my skin is in the summer when my body is tanned, and I want to match it up to my face.

4. Use concealer under eyes, and on any freckles or blemishes. Use this *very* gently under your eyes as this is the most delicate skin on your body.

5. With cream blusher, pat and contour colour into the most flattering curve of your cheek. Since there are so many different face shapes this can be different for everyone. Rule of thumb here – *blend*. Do not leave a hard line where the colour ends.

6. With a thick brown pencil gently line under the eyes, on the eyelids and up to the brow. Because I have a larger than normal space between my lid and brow I need this shadow here, but if you don't have a lot of space you may not need any.

7. With loose powder and a clean puff dust powder thickly over entire face, including lashes and neck. Brush off with a large sable brush and dab with water and cotton wool if you wish.

8. Take eyebrow pencil and gently darken brows. Make sure the curve suits the shape of your eye.

9. Outline upper eyelid with eyeliner. This can be extended to the outer corner if it suits you. If you are dark-haired, outline underneath the eyes too.

10. Mascara your top and bottom lashes and eyebrow hairs if they are thick enough.

11. With a lip pencil outline your lips, then fill in with the pencil. Blot with tissue, then apply preferred colour. The blotting and pencil beneath ensures that your lipstick will stay on for hours even while eating.

She never yet was foolish that was fair.

(OTHELLO
WILLIAM SHAKESPEARE)

MY SECRETS

12. Take a sable eye-shadow brush and apply powdered shadow on eyelid and slightly above, if you like the look.

13. Finally spritz your face with Evian water to set make-up, blot with Kleenex – and voilà! Ready to go. Once you get the hang of it this make-up should take you no longer than six or seven minutes.

MAKE-UP KNOW-HOW

☐ Always take your foundation and base down to your neck and over the ears – if you don't you will have a different coloured face and neck, which looks odd.

☐ When using eyeshadows and blushers don't forget that the darker colours minimise your bad points and the lighter colours accentuate your good points.

☐ A good way to achieve thick lashes is to apply mascara while sitting under the hair dryer. The hot air dries it fast, so you can apply several coats in succession.

☐ If eyelashes look clumpy when mascara is applied, separate them with another mascara wand, clean and damp.

☐ Throw away all old half-used mascaras, lipsticks, make-up bases. Anything that is more than two years old is bad for your skin, particularly anything you use around the eyes.

☐ Keep eyebrow pencils extremely pointed for the best effects.

☐ For a healthy look, use blusher on your cheekbones and in the centre of your forehead, under the chin and at the edges of your hairline. Blend carefully to avoid tide marks.

☐ If you are in a hurry to go out at night and have no time to remove make-up and start again, blot your face thoroughly with tissues until all excess oil is absorbed, then gently reapply a touch of base to the patchy areas around your nose and cheeks and chin. Powder thoroughly and reapply lip and eye make-up.

☐ Mascara brushed gently hair by hair on to the eyebrows makes them look natural, but needs a steady hand.

☐ If you run out of lip gloss use Vaseline; if you run out of face powder use talcum or baby powder; and if you run out of blusher blend your lipstick in the palm of your hand with a little cold cream.

☐ To minimise a double chin, use blusher around the jawbone, gradually fading colour under the jawline. Then apply a slightly darker

MY SECRETS

shade directly under the chin and blend.

☐ Blusher is the best quick make-up rejuvenator there is – it gives an instant glow and makes you look as if you've had eight hours' sleep. But blusher is supposed to make you look healthy, not as if you have a fever. Check your application with a hand mirror in profile before completing make-up.

☐ False eyelashes can look fabulous. To make them look natural, never wear them more than a millimetre longer than your own lashes; mascara them as you would your own, top and bottom; if they go straight and floppy wash them with soap and water and roll them around a pencil wrapped in a tissue – next day they will be as good as new.

☐ Never use stark white highlighter under your brows or on any other area. Try very pale pink or subtle greys and browns. Eyeshadow should emphasise your eyes, not your brand of eyeshadow.

☐ Don't try to change your natural skin tone. You were made a blonde, brunette or redhead, and extreme shades of basic foundation will look harsh and artificial.

MAKE-UP — A POTTED HISTORY

The ancient Egyptians believed that make-up was an art form, and you can see how varied and inventive their make-ups were on the sphinxes in museums. They had dozens of clever make-up tricks – how else would Cleopatra, never known for being a beauty, have snared Caesar *and* Mark Antony? The Cleopatra eye is still around today. I favour it sometimes as it is enormously effective on brunettes. The eye is rimmed with black liquid liner, or kohl as they used then, and drawn into a slanting 'doe-eye' shape in the corner.

Courtiers and aristocrats in the eighteenth century were so pock-marked, spotted, and pitted with acne and other skin conditions, that extremely heavy layers of lead-based paint were plastered on to disguise it. Since they seldom bathed, they used paint, powder and perfume to cover their skin and their smell. As dry cleaning had not been invented yet, the state of the satin and lace pastel ball gowns can only be imagined! But by the nineteenth century make-up was all but taboo for 'respectable' women. The most they could get away with was a dusting of rice powder on their nose, and finger pinching their cheeks to make

SOME OF MY FAVOURITE BEAUTIFIERS

TONER
Clinique Clarifying Lotion No. 1.

MOISTURISER
Clinique Dramatically Different Moisturising Lotion.

HAND & BODY LOTION
The Body Shop Rich Massage Lotion.

SOAP
(for body only) Neutrogena.

BATH OIL
Sardo (only in America I'm afraid) but Johnson's Baby Oil is good too.

FOUNDATION
Nobara U.V. Cream Foundation or Clinique Extra Help make-up.

FOUNDATION AND POWDER COMBINED
Kanebo Total Finish Foundation.

POWDER
Clinique Transparent Powder.

MASCARA
Chanel Noir Magique.

EYE LINER
Lancôme Traceur Matique Black.

EYE SHADOW
Chanel powders – any colours.

LIPSTICK
Imperial Formula or Christian Dior 'Framboise'.

BLUSHER
Revlon and Guerlain Terracotta powder.

EYEBROW PENCILS
Lancôme Le Crayon, Kohl, Black Coffee and Black Ebony.

CONCEALER
Renoir Special Cover 8 (only in America, but Chanel have a good one).

MAKE-UP REMOVER
Nivea skin oil.

NIGHT CREAM
Lancôme – Renergie.

FACE MASK
Masque Hydratant by Clarins.

SUN TAN OIL
Bain de Soleil by Antoine, Après Sun by Nivea.

MY SECRETS

them pink. Only loose women and actresses (never held in high esteem) used make-up.

The 1920s changed all that radically. Overnight it became accepted for women to paint and powder their faces to their heart's content. Many of the big make-up companies started then, Max Factor, Helena Rubenstein, Leichner. Faces were re-shaped as the 'flappers' painted their lips into carmine cupid's bows and tweezed their eyebrows to painted arcs of amazement. Pencilled brows, mascara, rouge, powder and lipstick were all applied with a heavy hand, and a woman wore her make-up with pride.

For the next several years, generations of women wore more or less the same make-up. There was not a vast range of colours vis-à-vis lipstick, eyeshadow or nail varnish to speak of, and a young girl would use the same products as her mother.

Then, in the 1950s everything changed. Companies like Revlon and Max Factor launched amazing new ranges of colours and textures, both in lipsticks, shadows and varnishes. In the 1960s false eyelashes were available for every woman. Previously only worn by film actresses, they now came in many colours, sometimes even encrusted with 'diamonds'. Bottom lashes were worn too, a look which has recently come back into style.

THE HOLLYWOOD LIFT!

Have you ever wondered why some movie stars look so good on the screen, yet if you see them in real life they look puffy, jowly and their skin seems to sag? That is probably because they have had what's known in the business as the Hollywood Lift. Make-up men have been doing it since the dawn of movies, because in the days of harsh black and white lighting, even a twenty-five-year-old actress would look as if she had shadows and furrows. Often the studio bosses' solution was simple. Get a younger actress, which is probably the reason why, in the days of silent movies and early talkies the studios hired their actresses young, and got rid of them before they were twenty-six or twenty-seven. This was the age which was then believed to be a woman's peak of beauty and perfection. This of course is still the norm with photographic and couture models, a girl being considered over the hill by the time she's in her late twenties. However, I'm glad to say that

MY SECRETS

female movie stars today are made of more lasting stock.

The following method, used by Marlene Dietrich in many of her films, is one of the ways in which you too could benefit, if you want to look especially fetching for some glamorous event, although I don't suggest doing this too often as pulling the skin weakens the underlying structure and stops blood circulating in the area. It *is* effective, but although I've only tried it once, it hurts!

1. Take a one-inch wide piece of hair near the front of each ear.
2. Make a tiny plait, pulling as tightly as you can.
3. Fasten the plait with a small elastic band.
4. Do the same to the other side, above the ear.
5. Lift the two braids to the top of the head, pulling them tightly so that the skin around them is pulled up too.
6. Attach the braids on to the top of the head with another elastic band. You can do this as tightly as you can. The tighter you do it the better the effect, but of course the worse for your skin.
7. Comb the rest of your hair over the elastic bands, or cover the whole thing with a head band, scarf, or wig.

You may find it necessary to change your eye make-up as this effect can dramatically change the way you look. Marlene Dietrich used to do these plaits not only just above her ears, but several of them all around her hairline, so that the tension pulled her entire face up. It must have been total agony but many women believed then that you had to suffer to be beautiful!

I've always been able to put my make-up on wherever and whenever I was. Bottom: On the set of *The Road to Hong Kong*, 1961. Below: In the Florida swamps in my least favourite film, 1977.

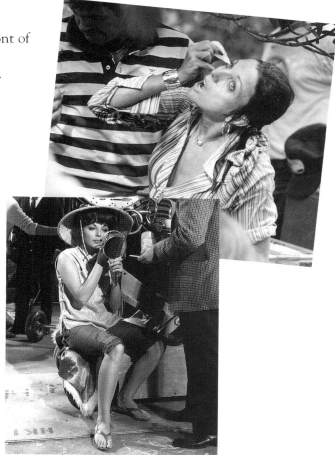

MY SECRETS

CHAPTER ELEVEN

Classic Clothes Sense

The butter wouldn't melt in her mouth look. A publicity still from one of my early British films. No, I never actually wore things like this at nineteen!

Opposite: The boots are what everyone will be wearing. Hard to do up, yes, but the look is great.

CLOTHES ARE MY passion – I adore them. Clothes reveal to the world what you think of yourself and I believe you should look well turned-out whatever you are doing. A white shirt and blue jeans can look more elegant for the right occasion than a power suit or cocktail dress, so when in doubt, dress down. Unless you have tons of confidence you'll feel foolish in an off the shoulder blouse and gypsy skirt if everyone around you is in sweat pants and T-shirts.

Today, because there are so many different ways to dress, and there are so many choices, women aren't sure how they want to look. Should you wear a skirt that just covers your rear, one down to your ankles, or a three-quarter-length skirt slit to the thigh? All are now acceptable, so we're spoilt for choice.

Many women today are fashion victims, even if they don't think they are. A 'fashion victim' is someone who wears anything unflattering, unsuitable, or overly faddish. Since almost all high fashion is designed by men, to be shown on the catwalk on the archetypal six foot, eighteen-year-old stick-thin supermodel, on whom a bin liner would look good, the average woman, hasn't a hope in hell of looking good in these clothes. The couture shows, in which the clothes are often as outrageous and over-the-top as possible, are designed for maximum publicity coverage in newspapers and magazines, but they don't really translate to the High Street. Each season the clothes seem to become more unflattering. Lycra leggings are fun, if you have reasonable legs. But bare midriffs? Grunge? Frumpy see-through granny dresses? They look to me like layers of rags and they cost thousands. I flicked through a recent issue of a fashion magazine in utter astonishment. Why now more than ever are women being cajoled into emulating skinny teenaged girls in rags? It seems that certain designers want to make women look foolish. Is it because many of them don't really *like* real women? They adore beautiful *girls* of course – but *real* women, with all their flaws, don't interest them.

Some of the designers who love and appreciate real women and who design clothes to flatter them include Donna Karan, Valentino, Yves St. Laurent, Nolan Miller, Gian-Franco Ferre at Dior, Anouska Hempel and many more. The designers who *do* try to make women look attractive are often sneered at by the chic fashion press, accused of being old fashioned. But new does not necessarily mean good and all too often it is hideously unflattering. Five years ago, when *Dynasty* was all the rage, I and all the other actresses in the show wore power suits and women viewers loved how we looked, but it was much criticised by the fashion pundits. The most attractive and practical outfit for a career woman, business woman or almost any woman for that matter was slagged off consistently for years for being boring. But what could be more comfortable, stylish and easy to wear than a shirt, a tailored jacket and pants, or a medium length, straight skirt? I agree, however, that our *Dynasty* shoulders sometimes got *too* big, and sometimes the clothes were over the top.

When I started in the show, all the other actresses wore simple silk shirts and gaberdine trousers or skirts. I thought that was boring, so when I came on the scene, I persuaded the designer Nolan Miller to let me wear haute couture clothes with padded shoulders. Some of my early outfits were quite elegant. Then everyone suddenly wanted to become chic, so Nolan had to make me more outrageous than the others to fit in with my character. My shoulder pads got bigger and bigger – my hats more bizarre, my heels higher, my skirts shorter: it became ridiculous and I became the butt of many a female imposter's drag act! But have you seen any Joan Crawford, Bette Davis or Lana Turner 1940s movies recently? Those women looked divine, 100 per cent better than most of today's screen heroines, and their shoulder pads were huge! A suit is completely timeless and *always*

Above: By the late 1980s, the shoulder detail on evening gowns was becoming so enormous that even getting through a doorway was a major effort! With Jeffrey Lane, Los Angeles, 1987.

Opposite: Rather a fabulous evening dress by Nolan Miller, 1987. This style of elaborate gown is now rarely worn except for very grand events.

MY SECRETS

Feathers never go out of fashion. Here is my Aunt Lalla starring in *Sunny* in the 1930s, and me in *Blondes vs Brunettes* in 1985. Opposite: Classic glamour as revealed in the 1980s in the mini-series *Sins*. This was the look of the late 1960s.

will be. I still wear Yves St Laurent or Valentino jackets and trousers from ten years ago, and I will probably be wearing them ten years from now. You certainly can't say the same for grunge dresses and sequin flares.

The women I admire don't slavishly follow fashion, but adapt their own particular look fluidly and elegantly each season. I can't imagine Princess Diana visiting a hospice in a bustier and fringed patchwork layers. She usually wears a simple suit and looks simple, practical and elegant.

So don't be fooled. The jacket and skirt will go on *forever*, trust me. What else looks good in the office or the boardroom, at dinner, at the theatre or boarding an airplane? You can't go wrong with a suit.

. . .

Many of the women whose fashion sense I admire are usually under- rather than over-dressed. (I come from a family of aunts and grandmas whose tendency was always to put on a little bit more. That extra brooch, a feathered hat with a veil, *and* a flower, plus a necklace or two. Always just a touch *de trop*.)

Here is *my* list of women, in no particular order, whom I consider to be well dressed while still retaining their own special style: Princess Diana, Lynn Wyatt, Audrey Wilder, Inès de la Fressange, Shakira Caine, Iman, Princess Caroline of Monaco, the late Audrey Hepburn and Blaine Trump.

CREATING YOUR WARDROBE

I would advise any woman wanting to create a practical wardrobe to persuade a close friend to go through your clothes with you and start by getting rid of your mistakes. She will tell you, you've always looked hideous in that tomato-coloured blouse and help you chuck it. When you've cleared out from your wardrobe the things you no longer wear, the bad impulse buys, clothes that don't fit, now is the time to start organising and making a list of what you need to get a good, practical wardrobe that works for you.

Don't look at a photograph of Kim Basinger in a pink Lycra dress

and buy one, thinking that you're going to look just like her. Take a friend shopping, whose opinion you trust, and make sure you examine yourself in a three-way mirror when you try anything on. It's very important to be able to see yourself from all angles, since everybody else does. It's a good idea to buy separates with which to create different looks. If, for example, you buy a Donna Karan black 'body', you could wear it with a matching black skirt, black stockings, high-heels and big fake pearls and make it into a cocktail outfit. Or you could wear the same black body with blue jeans and a casual scarf around the waist for a more informal look. You can wear the body under a plain or check shirt and a jacket for daytime and office use, or under a white man's shirt for any time at all. You *must* buy items of clothing that you can use in as many different ways as possible. You may have to make a rather heavy initial investment, but it will definately pay off in the long run.

Being 'well dressed' means different things to different people. To a teenager it means her special battered jeans, baseball cap and a T-shirt with a slogan scrawled all over it. To a glamorous young model or actress who is into grunge, it could mean trendy layered rags, a floral dress with Doc Martens or the dandy look.

So many people today consider style, elegance, and being well-dressed a frivolous waste of time and irrelevant in the 1990s. I'm talking here to a woman whose idea of fashion and style is not torn blue jeans, or a shell suit (surely one of the ugliest outfits ever invented?). This woman wants to look her best in well-fitting, modern clothes that bring out the best in her without screaming, 'Look at me.' It's important to survey what you already possess, weed out and then get organised. Of course you may have to get rid of seventy per cent of your clothes, but the rule is, if you haven't worn something in eighteen months, you won't, until it comes back into fashion. And since that could easily be fifteen or twenty years, you can't afford the space. Not even Imelda Marcos has that many closets.

A three-way mirror is one of the most important investments you can make. You don't actually have to buy one – you can put one inside the door of your wardrobe and another nearby so that you can see

Opposite: This was one of the great popular looks of the 1960s. A 'John Lennon' cap in tweed matched with a suit. We recreated this for the mini-series *Sins* in 1985. I would wear it today.

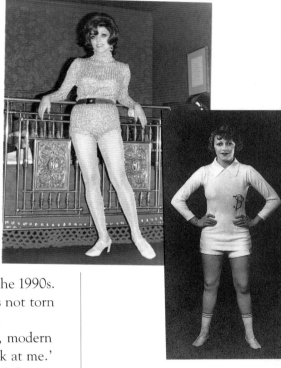

If you hang on to anything it will come back into fashion. Here is my Aunt Pauline in her hot-pants in the 1930s, and here am I in my gold lurex hot-pants in the 1970s. This is not a look I recommend for the over-thirties, unless you are going to the beach.

MY SECRETS

yourself from all angles, particularly the back. The changing rooms in the stores today don't stress the back view – even in expensive boutiques and couture houses.

Ask your friend or your daughter if something looks good – amazingly seven and eight-year-olds have an objective eye about what suits their mothers.

My own daughters have asked, having seen photographs of me in rather bizarre 1960s and 1970s gear, 'Mummy, *why* didn't you keep it?'

Well, the answer is, who has the space? And who has the foresight to know that in twenty years that Paco Rabanne bottle green sequin micro-mini dress is going to be the height of fashion again?

Since we don't want to clutter our wardrobes, we must be ruthless, even if our future grandchildren, surveying the family album, sigh covetously over that fuschia scarf dress you've long since dumped.

After you've weeded, make a pile of discards for Oxfam. You'll be amazed at how much you get rid of, and how much room you then have left for your new purchases. You can't do all this in one day so take your time and then think seriously what you want to keep hanging on those empty hangers.

Here is a list of what I consider to be basics for a modern, well-dressed, and classic look:

The classic black dress as worn in Hollywood in the 1950s.

JACKETS

You'll need at least two. Unfitted but simply cut, one should be black, like a blazer (perhaps with gold buttons), and one a neutral colour, tweed or beige. These jackets should be able to be worn over every other piece of clothing in your wardrobe and will probably be the most expensive items you buy. There are of course some marvellous jackets in chain-stores for under £100, which only an expert could differentiate from a designer label. Although fashion pundits have been advocating 'no more shoulder pads', don't listen. Shoulder pads are needed for the proper structure and tailoring of a jacket (have you ever seen a man's jacket without?).

SKIRTS

Once again the dreaded skirt debate is upon us. How long? How short? Who cares? As long as you've got the legs for it, above the knee is fine.

MY SECRETS

MY FAVOURITE
DEPARTMENT
STORES

Bloomingdales in
New York
Neiman Marcus in
Los Angeles
Harrods and Harvey
Nichols in London
Galeries Lafayette in Paris
Brown Thomas in Dublin

A stark but glamorous
1994 Yves St Laurent pant
suit. Black, with diamanté
buttons. St Laurent has been
doing variations of this suit
for a dozen years. And it is
very successful with all
women.

All the French designers tried desperately hard in their winter couture collections of 1992 to prove that the mini, or short skirt was out. Department stores filled up with the long length, and many women (including me because I like long skirts and think they are elegant) jumped on the bandwagon and wore long exclusively. Until, that is, the 1993 Paris winter couture collections, where all the designers (with the exception of Valentino) showed skirts so short that in some of them the model's bottom showed! When a friend who had invested heavily in the long skirts wailed to a top Paris couturier, 'But you said short skirts were finished and we should only wear long!' he answered rather cynically, 'Oh, you didn't buy into *that* too, did you?'

So I recommend having two skirts, black, neutral, short or long – whichever you feel more comfortable in. One full-length silk jersey or velvet, in either black or a jewel colour for evening and a tweed, tartan, or neutral skirt, all of which will go with your jackets.

SHIRTS

Buy as many classic simple shirts as you can afford. Four is the minimum you need; at least two white – one cotton, one silk or man-made fibre; one black, and one striped or patterned. You should collect shirts, but the plainer the better.

BODIES AND T-SHIRTS

You will need several 'bodies', or very simple plain T-shirts to go under the jackets to change your looks. 'Shells' are very inexpensive at the chain-stores and come in all colours in cotton or silk. They can also be worn over a shirt for a different layered look, or you can wear two contrasting ones together.

TROUSERS

If your jeans don't fit well, get rid of them. Nothing looks worse than ill-fitting jeans. The Gap have an excellent selection and you should eventually find a pair to suit you although it *will* take time. Buying jeans is, I have found, more time-consuming than buying practically anything else. We tend to think of jeans as very casual wear, but they can be extremely chic if worn with a man's white shirt, a great looking belt and proper shoes. (*Not* trainers. Nothing looks good with trainers in my

MY SECRETS

opinion, except shorts; they are also terribly bad for your feet if worn all the time, causing the arches to fall and feet to spread.) At least two pairs of trousers, one black, the other neutral. If you've a limited budget, stick to plain straight cut pants à la Armani and leave the flares to your daughter, because that's one fad that won't last.

ONE OR TWO WAISTCOATS

A black one, which can quickly change the look of any of your outfits, and a brocade or patterned one. The 'Oscar Wilde' dandy look is fashionable which you can create with a waistcoat and a scarf or a cravat.

COATS

Do many of us wear proper coats any more? English winters have been getting milder, so a raincoat (classic please, black or beige) is essential. If you can invest in another coat it should be very long, almost ankle length, military style, and big enough to wear over your jackets and shirts. Black, grey or navy blue are best.

FOOTWEAR

You'll need one pair of black boots – since this is the main colour in your wardrobe, one pair of high-heeled black leather shoes and one medium height, one pair of neutral shoes to wear with the plaid or plain pants and shirts, and one pair of very casual shoes to wear with jeans. They could be trainers, but I prefer espadrilles or loafers.

SWEATERS

A couple of sweaters at least: a black poloneck is one of the most essential components of any woman's wardrobe. A V-neck man's sweater is also quite useful and easy to wear. Fancy sweaters with patterns and slogans have no place in your basic wardrobe.

DRESSES

Hardly any women wear dresses any more. If you're going to buy just one dress I would invest in a plain black strapless, or cap-sleeved silk or jersey draped dress. It can be long, mid-calf, or short; it doesn't matter as long as it flatters your body. This can be worn with pearls or other

Some of the latest looks for 1994. Krizia designed this stunning double breasted completely plain grey cashmere and flannel trouser suit with matching trench coat. Absolutely fabulous!

Opposite: This Bruce Oldfield black dress is a knock-out and could be worn for practically any evening occasion.

MY SECRETS

costume jewellery for a black-tie dinner. It can go under your black jacket for theatre or dinner, and it can be worn to practically any social function at night, dressed up or down.

Good accessories say more about an individual than any other piece of her clothing, and although they can sometimes be a budget stretcher, the following should be considered as essential:

BAGS

Three bags – the best quality you can buy. All black, one Chanel style shoulder bag with the gold chain which is a classic and definitely here to stay. One small 'clutch' for evening, restaurants, theatre etc. and one 'tote' type for office, travel and everyday. I hate cheap bags, and, like the women of Italy and France I would rather have one good one than lots of cheapos.

BELTS

Two or three belts. A plain black one, leather or suede. A gold chain, and perhaps a Western style belt tooled leather with a silver or gold buckle.

JEWELLERY

Here's where you can go mad. Costume jewellery is so abundant and relatively inexpensive that an investment of several pieces, to which you can add over the years is essential. Although many people think jewellery is unnecessary, in my opinion it can make or break an outfit. Too much can kill it, but too little makes no impact. I have seen pictures of myself in magazines and shuddered as I've seen the results of my over-enthusiastic application of the *faux* jewel.

My aunts, great aunts and grandmother, who always adored the dressed-up look, usually stuck on an extra flower, brooch or bow somewhere . Of course half the fun of dressing up is putting on bits and pieces, but when you've put them on it's best to take most of them off again before you venture out.

Here are the essential items you should have in your jewellery box:
□ Two or three ropes of pearls of various lengths; pearls are extremely versatile (on the cover I'm wearing a necklace as a bracelet), and are the most flattering of all jewels. Two or three types extremely

My favourite white lace Valentino suit looks good with enormous chandelier earrings.

Opposite: Jet is back with a vengeance. My grandmother's necklace was brought out of the attic to wear at the BAFTA awards, London, 1993.

MY SECRETS

versatile (on the cover I'm wearing a necklace as a bracelet), and are the most flattering of all jewels. Two or three types of pearl earrings, ranging from the small stud type to large drops – *always* a great and glamorous look.

☐ A pair of gold studs or hoops; I'm quite partial to the gypsy look, which suits most brunettes, so I wear big gold earrings quite often.

☐ A couple of pins or brooches; *don't* wear these with a necklace as well though. It might look good in a magazine, but in life it's overkill.

☐ Rhinestone or diamanté earrings: as many as you can collect. I'm a fiend for costume jewellery. It's the one thing in the clothes line that is collectable and doesn't take up too much space.

☐ The best watch you can buy, but the simplest. I loathe gimmicky watches except on children.

☐ I believe that rings should always be real, so if you haven't got a real one, don't wear one. By real, I mean it could be silver, or jade or any of the reasonably priced semi-precious stones that are available.

☐ A fake flower, white or black; a gardenia is my favourite à la Chanel, but I think a flower in the lapel or on the shoulder can be extremely alluring.

☐ Gold chains – beware of too many. The gold chain look can be very 1980s if overdone. One or two look best, and they can be mixed with the pearls.

☐ Scarves – I collect these too. A scarf can *totally* change a jacket and skirt. There are hundreds of ways to wear a scarf, and since there are so many variations, it's up to you to experiment.

☐ Bracelets are really non-essential items. Wear them if you like but I would rather concentrate on earrings and necklaces than bracelets, particularly if the budget is limited.

I've rarely not worn a sun bonnet. On Brighton beach with Mummy and Nanny. I wore a protective sun hat even then!

☐ I'm crazy about hats and have loads of them. I know that most women today don't wear hats but there are going to be occasions in your life, a wedding for example, when you will need a hat. I believe that a hat should be simple. A brimmed hat (and it can be a big brim if you're tall enough) is always more flattering that one without. It can have some decoration, but excessiveness in the hat department only suits the Queen Mother! The crown should be neither

too flat nor too high and it should fit. Pillboxes and gimmicky shapes are only good for race meetings once a year. If you get a hat, make sure it's a classic and never buy one unless you've looked at yourself in a full length mirror carefully.

Fashion passes, style remains. Find your style and stick to it. Just remember you are your own work of art and there is no one else who looks like you. The real secret of good dressing is to be individual and stylish enough to make a statement about yourself that is original, attractive and fun, and yet not be so over-the-top that you are uncomfortable and inhibited.

Your personality is projected through your clothes, but you must not be self-conscious when wearing something new or a bit different. If you feel that what you are wearing is not attractive you will not feel confident and people will react to you negatively. What you wear should always provoke a positive reaction.

SOME OF MY FAVOURITE CLOTHES BRANDS

SHOES
Manolo Blahnik

TIGHTS
Calvin Klein; Donna Karan

BRAS
Rigby & Peller; Marks & Spencer

PANTS
Marks & Spencer

JEWELLERY
(Real) Cartier (if old), Theo Fennell (if new)

JEWELLERY
(Costume) Kenneth J. Lane

TROUSERS
Armani; Joseph

SKIRTS
Karl Lagerfeld; Next

SHIRTS
Chanel; Donna Karan; Versace

BELTS
Chanel; Hermès

EVENING DRESSES
Valentino; Anouska Hempel; Christian Lacroix

JACKETS
Valentino; Versace

BATHING SUITS
Gottex

BIKINIS
The St Tropez beach boutiques

SUITS
Dior; Chanel; Max Mara

HATS
Philip Somerville

STRAW HATS
Herbert Johnson; Patricia Underwood

JEANS
Calvin Klein; The Gap

SHOULDER BAGS
Chanel

EVENING BAGS
Judith Leiber

HAND BAGS
Hermès

NIGHTGOWNS
Dior; Marks & Spencer

BODIES AND SHIRTS
Donna Karan

SILK PYJAMAS
Hong Kong's Stanley Road stalls ($20 and beautiful!)

SCARVES
Charvet; Hermès

SUNGLASSES
Ray Bans; Joan Collins Collection (Yes! they're great and they'll be in a shop near you soon!)

Top: I prefer wearing this to bed than an old T-shirt!
Above: Glasses can add to your appearance. These are my own design – Joan Collins Eyewear. Yes, you can buy them here too!

MY SECRETS

CHAPTER TWELVE

Women and Love

THERE HAVE PROBABLY been more words written about sex and love in all their forms than any other activity human beings indulge in. As we become more and more open about sex, more women are confused about it. Every women's magazine is packed with articles about sex, giving readers advice about what to do, how to feel, how to enjoy it more, and how many times the average person should have sex in a week, a month, a year! I believe there is no such thing as the norm. If you only make love two or three times a month or a year, what does it matter, as long as you both enjoy it. Sex isn't just something that can be turned on like a tap.

Of course, just as there are alcoholics, chocoholics and foodaholics so there are sexaholics; people who are so hung up on the adrenalin-fuelled thrill of a new relationship, that they spend their lives searching for it. They need the admiration and approval of a new partner; that is what boosts their self-esteem. Passionate sex, that heart thumping feeling of being with the beloved love object, heightens their sense of sexual awareness, and makes them feel more alive. However, when a more personal commitment beckons, they usually panic, end the relationship, and go in search of the next passionate experience.

Most women and men don't have the libido of a young boy who may have sex a dozen times a day. I read recently that a famous actress and her husband, both in their thirties, make love ten times a day! Surely very few women would want to do that. As with everything else, it is quality not quantity that counts. Making love two or three times a

A good man nowadays is hard to find, but Alexis found Dex (Michael Nader) in 1985 on *Dynasty*.

day with your partner is supposedly 'normal' on honeymoon and at the beginning of a passionate relationship; after that perhaps two or three times a week might be enough. But it depends entirely on the individuals concerned.

In a marriage or long-term relationship often the man wants sex automatically, without any foreplay. His attitude is that he doesn't need to bother and that he has a right to have sex with his wife. Women definitely need more time to get sexually aroused. They need tender loving care, romance and love, and those who say they don't are denying their true femininity.

Many women find that as they get older, or after they have had babies, their interest in sex decreases. They start to dislike the changes happening to their bodies, and thinking that they can't measure up to the ideals of beauty when they see gorgeous models in commercials and magazines, they feel undesirable. With decreasing self-esteem they become more inhibited about revealing their bodies during sex and soon the whole procedure becomes a vicious circle. The more the woman turns away from sex, the more the man does too.

Many people feel that sex should be the prerogative of the young, sometimes only the very young, and that anybody over the age of 40 shouldn't be sexually active. This is nonsense; sex should be as healthy and natural a part of life as eating or drinking. But there is nothing worse than having to eat when you are not hungry, and having to make love when you don't feel like it, even if you love that person, can be upsetting.

Unfortunately, many women still feel that they have to 'please their man', and so they allow their partner to make love when they are not feeling up to it.

As you get older you will have more time for sex. The children are gone, you are not as tired as you were and you have time to get to know your husband or partner better. And sex does not always have to mean intercourse; cuddling, being close in bed, or on the sofa watching television together, holding hands, sharing intimacies, can be just as sexy and sexual as making love. The loving togetherness that two people can have can be extremely sexy. It is certainly much sexier than throwing yourself around in bars and discos. Most women *do* put sex and love into the same compartment but fail to understand that many

You cannot be wise, and in love at the same time.

MY SECRETS

men do not. Sex can mean something different for men than it does for women and that is a lesson we should all teach our daughters. As they say, 'Women go to bed with men so that they can talk to them. Men talk to women so they can go to bed with them.'

The principal clinical psychologist at the Royal Edinburgh Hospital, Dr David Weeks, has been doing research for several years on why some people look so much younger than others. He has found by questioning over two thousand men and women, 'They all come across as happy, nice people who enjoy sex both in terms of quality and quantity. They make love more often than other people, and they are very physical and tactile. Although they have more partners than average, they usually remain friends with their lovers. They are romantic, tend to fall in love a lot, and are positive thinkers. They do not just have sex for the sake of sex, it involves long-term caring about the other person.'

The good news for those who enjoy making love is continue doing it, and you'll look and feel better. After all we don't stop sexual activity because we grow old – we grow old because we stop sexual activity. In our culture it is not considered 'nice' for older people to be having sex, we don't want to know about it, or discuss it. But sexual interest and activity help keep the adrenal and sex glands producing hormones, which keep you young by stimulating and enhancing practically all of the body's vital functions. That should be good news for everyone over forty. Getting older means that you should have earned the right to do what you want when you want to do it, and if that means having either more or less sex, so be it.

I think many of the reasons why more and more older women are involved in relationships with, or married to younger men, is that they don't have to put up with a certain patronising, sexist attitude, because younger men have been brought up believing that women are equal. A man in his twenties and thirties today is quite different from a man in his forties, fifties or sixties. Older men usually wouldn't dream of helping with the washing up, the shopping or cooking, but younger men are more attuned to sharing, more sensitive and more willing to be flexible.

All the traditional dating games were thrown out of the window in the 1960s, which is sad, because I do think that early in a

After ecstasy, the laundry.

(ZEN STATEMENT)

relationship a certain amount of game-playing is necessary. If you throw yourself all over a man just after you've been to bed with him, you can forget it! As the comedienne Rita Rudner says: 'When I want to break up with a guy, I don't tell him I don't love him any more – it's over. No way he'll leave. No. I say 'Honey, I love you, I want to move in with you, I want to have your baby.' You can hear the skidmarks as he takes off!'

When people think of sex they usually think of intercourse only, but to many, sex can be just kissing, cuddling and being close. Men and women often feel guilty because they don't feel like having sex every minute of the day, but sex in a relationship is naturally very cyclical. There may be times when you don't feel like it, or times when he doesn't. It doesn't mean either of you have gone off each other; it's just one of life's natural rhythms.

Sex can be the greatest thing in the world. It can also be the worst, if one of the participants doesn't want it. Sex has to be a balanced part of a balanced life, but women must be careful not to confuse sex with love, because men never have done, even if they pretend to.

. . .

Women are life-givers, and love-givers. Not only do we give birth, but we nurture our babies, care for them, love them unconditionally, and bring them up to adulthood as best we can. When we get pregnant, millions of 'I want a baby' hormones course through our bodies, steering our minds towards motherhood.

Men, of course, often do not feel this way. Although there are more single parent mothers in America and England today, there don't seem to be many single parent fathers. Frequently, a woman is left holding the baby, while the man goes off to get on with his life. Even if she *can* afford a child-minder, she will find it tough to live her own life. There's too much blame attached to unmarried girls who have babies, and then, unable to work, have to live off welfare. Why should only the girls get the blame? What about the men? It takes two to make a baby, and society should come down much more strongly on any man who impregnates a girl, then runs off with no consideration, no penalty, and no conscience.

What a line up of buses. In *Male Model* I played an agent who had her pick of the hunks on her books.

MY SECRETS

Most women once they become mothers are mothers for life, and the majority care for their children and do all they can for them. My children are in their twenties, but I still talk to them practically every day and see them as much as I can. I try not to worry about them but they are foremost in my mind before I go to sleep at night, and first thing when I wake up in the morning.

The fact is that most women choose to try and live as peaceful and caring a life as possible, loving our families, our children and our friends around us, and trying to make the best of our environments. Most women are warm, nurturing, tender and caring. If I had a really serious emotional problem, I'd certainly call on a woman friend to help me, because I know she would understand.

I am *not* anti-men by any means. I like men, and I have many wonderful men friends – men who are caring, considerate, wonderful fathers, men who are gentle, amusing, hard-working and dedicated. But

Top: Judy Bryer and I have been friends for 26 years and I hope we will be for many more. Los Angeles, 1987.

Above: All the world's a stage and when Christopher Biggins and I stepped out with the statues in Baden-Baden we painted the town red. Germany, 1993.

I have met some uncaring beasts who treat women abominably. What many men don't realise is that bringing up children is one of the most exhausting jobs in the world. When my children were under two, I barely had time to comb my hair. If you really love and care for your children, you put 100 per cent of yourself into them.

The expectations of modern women today are enormous; and if we don't live up to them we feel guilty. We try to give 100 per cent to our children, 100 per cent to our jobs, 100 per cent to the men in our lives, and because there's no such thing as a 300 per cent person, we think we've failed and then we feel guilty for failing.

The guilt of working mothers can be intense. I know sometimes I felt it strongly. Yet I had to pay those bills. There is still an assumption that if you go out to work, you must be a bad mother. Many mothers *need* to work for financial reasons, and sometimes psychological ones. To want a career shouldn't make a woman feel guilty. Guilt is an entirely negative emotion; it doesn't help your children if you feel guilty about working, nor does it help your work. If that guilt finally stops you working, you may just end up resenting your children. The fear that they may grow up and blame you for not being with them twenty-four

MY SECRETS

hours a day shouldn't be a motivating factor in your decision. Don't forget, children grow up and eventually leave *you*.

You also may not function so well as a mother if you're secretly feeling the need for a career as well. We feel even more guilty as mothers if, as in half the marriages in America and a third in Britain, ours end in divorce. I know how badly I felt when I divorced Tony – my children were only three and five. I went through agony, feeling that I was ruining my children's lives. For some time up to this point, I had felt the need to stay married for the children's sake. But after a year or so of trying, I realised I couldn't.

It's hard to be a good mother if you're in the middle of a bad marriage. Unfortunately, I went through it twice, and altogether have spent over five years staying in marriages that didn't work because of the guilt. In my last marriage, when after thirteen months I knew it wasn't working and since there were no children involved, I ended the farce quickly. I found a lawyer and moved out of the house. It was hard, but I knew I had done the right thing for *me*. Spending years in an impossible relationship eats away at one's positivity. Guilt should never be a motivating force in a decision.

With some of my closest friends I can really relax. Pandora Delevingne, Louise Fennell, Charles Delevingne, Theo Fennell and Lynn Wyatt. St Tropez, 1992.

. . .

Love still makes the world go round. To love and be loved is the most important thing in life. All those tired old clichés are still, strangely enough, unbelievably apt. Love is still the cherry on top of the icing on the cake of life, and hopefully we will continue to make those moments the happiest and most fulfilling of our lives.

MY SECRETS

CHAPTER THIRTEEN

A-Z of All Things Good and Bad

GOOD THINGS

APPLE

The apple is one of the most healing and beneficial fruits in existence. The adage 'an apple a day keeps the doctor away' is not just an old wives' tale; it has long been recognised a health tonic, bowel regulator and healing medicine. It contains natural substances which help prevent digestive and liver troubles. It stimulates the extrication of digestive juices and is a good source of vitamin C, an antioxidant essential for good health. Apples also contain natural fruit sugar and supply over a dozen minerals, including iron, iodine, potassium, sulphur, calcium, and amino acids.

Eating an apple an hour before exercising will give you a quick energy boost. A good way to lose a few pounds and also make yourself feel terrific is to go on an apple fast for a couple of days. All you need to do is eat as many apples as you want in place of regular meals, three or four times a day. You must eat *every single* piece of the apple, including peel, seeds and core and chew it until the last drop. Apples can be grated, sprinkled with cinnamon on top, or put in a blender with water to make a delicious drink.

AVOCADO

This luscious, nutritious pear is almost a complete food in itself and one of the best inner beauty foods you can eat. Although the avocado is not a slimming food, its benefits far outweigh the extra calories. Avocados are rich in potassium and the antioxidant, vitamin E, which helps combat the deadly free radicals which are one of the premier causes of ageing.

The avocado pear contains pure avocado oil, one of the best natural oils there is, which feeds the skin inside as well as out. I recommend eating two or three avocados a week as a treat for your skin. Compensate for the extra calories by cutting out a

piece of bread, pasta, or the rough equivalent of 190 calories from your diet. After you have eaten an avocado, massage your body lightly with the skin. Leave on for 15 minutes, then rinse off with warm water.

Make yourself an excellent skin mask with:
½ avocado peeled and puréed
1 dessert-spoonful of pure honey
55ml whole milk

Mix ingredients in blender until you have the consistency of paste. Apply to your neck and face and leave for 15 minutes. Rinse off with cool water.

You can also use the shell to smooth rough skin on the soles of your feet and elbows.

BANANA
The banana is one of the greatest convenience foods ever and, contrary to popular belief, is not high in calories – it actually contains on average only 60 calories. Whenever I crave something sweet a banana usually satisfies that craving. Bananas are extremely good for the digestive system. High in carbohydrates with a complete range of complex sugars, they are digested slowly, so that a constant stream of energy is released throughout the body. They take between 45 minutes and an hour to absorb (twice as much as other fruits) which is probably why they are the favourite snack fruit for many athletes. Bananas also contain potassium.

A banana makes a great face mask and leaves the skin soft. Mash a banana, spread it over the face, leave it on for 10 minutes, then rinse off

with cold water. This banana paste is also an excellent conditioner for hair. Leave on for 15 minutes after shampooing normally, then rinse off.

BEETROOT
Beetroot juice enriches the blood, which is why it has been used for centuries to build up resistance and treat convalescents. Fresh, raw beetroot juice is a powerful tonic; it cleanses the blood, and is extremely beneficial to the digestive system. Try raw beetroot, grated with raw carrot and cucumber for a healthy salad. Most people prefer their beetroot cooked, but drenching it in vinegar only negates the beneficial properties of this highly nutritious vegetable.

BROCCOLI
The National Cancer Institute of America conducted a study which proved broccoli has more cancer-protecting properties than any other vegetable. Broccoli is without doubt my favourite vegetable and I am a fervent believer in its health promoting powers. The darker and greener a vegetable is, the better, and you can't get darker or greener than broccoli. It is extremely rich in iron, so if you are anaemic, exhausted, or anxious you should eat plenty of it. I try to eat broccoli at least every other day, steamed, raw, hot, cold, served with salads, fish or chicken, or just by itself.

If you need a really fast and efficient diet, try eating nothing but broccoli and tomatoes for two days. Not only will you feel quite full, but you will lose weight so rapidly that you will be able to get into that new bathing suit.

I didn't have a leading man in *The Opposite Sex* so they gave me these instead. MGM, 1956.

Here is one of my favourite broccoli recipes which is delicious served with fish, chicken or veal:

BROCCOLI WITH ALMONDS

·FOR 4 PEOPLE·
1 large head of broccoli
45g whole almonds
1 cup of fresh white breadcrumbs
1 clove garlic (optional)
30g olive oil

Break broccoli into sprigs and trim stalks slightly. Steam for 7-10 minutes. Blanch almonds, shred and soak for half an hour in a little water. Drain well. Fry almonds lightly with the breadcrumbs in the oil until golden brown. Season well, adding garlic. Arrange broccoli in a serving dish and scatter breadcrumb mixture over the top.

CALCIUM

Because I drink several cups of coffee a day I try to make up for it by taking calcium in tablet form. The recommended daily dose is 700 mg, and since we cannot have healthy and strong bones as we get older without an adequate supply of calcium, it is vitally important for the over forties to take it as a supplement or in the following foods: sardines (an excellent source. Eat a whole tin at least twice a week with the bones and some of the oil), salmon, tofu, dairy products, dates, spinach, low-fat yogurt, seaweed, sesame seeds, broccoli, red kidney beans.

DATES

Another of what I consider magic foods, dates are packed with natural sugar. They are also rich in magnesium, calcium and copper. Highly nourishing, they are particularly good if you are recovering from an illness. A Bedouin Arab can travel for days across the desert, with only water, dates and flour to make bread. In some Arab countries dates are also considered a sexual stimulant! They are also mildly laxative and make an excellent sugar-free alternative to a pastille for a sore throat as they lubricate the lungs. (Don't forget to take the stone out first!)

Dates can be served hot or cold with yoghurt or cream as a delicious dessert. You can replace the pit with a piece of marzipan or a nut and serve after dinner instead of mints or chocolates.

Here is one of my favourite recipes for date slices:

DATE SLICES

·MAKES 14·
150g low-fat margarine
175g rolled oats
100g plain wholewheat flour
225g stoned dates
1 × 15ml spoon lemon juice
1 × 15ml spoon honey
a few drops of vanilla essence

Turn the oven to 180°C/Gas mark 4/350°F. Grease a 7"/18cm square tin. Simmer dates in 2 × 15ml spoons water over a gentle heat for about 10 minutes, i.e. until soft.

Remove from the heat and stir in lemon juice, honey and vanilla essence. Put the oats and flour in a bowl and rub in the margarine. Press half of the oat mixture into the tin. Spread the date mixture over the oat mixture in the tin, then cover with

the rest of the oat mixture and press down firmly. Bake for about 25 minutes, until golden brown. Cut into slices while still warm, then leave to cool in the tin. Absolutely fabulous! And children love them.

EGGS

Egg yolks contain lecithin, an organic phosphorized fat, and an essential nutrient. They also contain good quality protein so they are extremely nutritious for young children, but should not be eaten to excess since the egg yolk contains cholesterol.

It is best when cooking with eggs to use 1 yolk per 3 whites. Scrambled eggs can taste just as good this way even though they will probably not be as yellow.

Many doctors now think that women should eat no more than two eggs a week, as some research has linked too many eggs to breast cancer, and eggs definitely increase cholesterol levels.

I love eggs but am quite wary of them. I particularly like them hard boiled and mashed with a small amount of low-fat mayonnaise. With a sliced tomato and two crispbreads this makes a satisfying and extremely low-calorie lunch.

Eggs are one of the oldest beauty treatments in existence; Cleopatra is said to have used the white of a whipped egg as a soothing face mask and skin tightener, and I know some women who still do.

Here are a two excellent beauty treatments using the humble egg:

FACE MASK

1 egg yolk
1 teaspoon almond oil

Mix together and apply to face. Rinse off after 15 minutes.

EGG AND YEAST REVITALIZING
MASK

1 egg yolk
1 tablespoon sunflower oil
1 tablespoon brewer's yeast

Mix into a smooth paste. Apply gently to face (not around the eye area). Rinse off with warm water or milk after 15 minutes.

EVENING
PRIMROSE OIL

Evening primrose oil has many other names. It is sometimes called king's cure-all, sands lily, rock rose, sun drop, night willow-herb, coffee plant, fever plant. A main ingredient in EPO is Gamma Linolenic Acid (GLA), essential to health because it is needed to make a family of hormone-type compounds that control all the organs in the body, especially the skin, heart, and circulation. An excellent mechanism against disease, EPO is a dietary supplement that I, and many of my friends, swear by. Scientists do not know exactly how or why it has an effect on the body, however. But evening primrose oil has been known to lead to weght-loss without dieting, to lower blood cholesterol and blood pressure, and heal or improve eczema and rheumatoid arthritis. It can also relieve pre-menstrual pain and clear acne.

There is something mystical about evening primrose oil, and research is continuing on the subject all the time.

MY SECRETS

FIBRE

Fibre is one of the essential ingredients needed for proper elimination. But today unfortunately we do not eat nearly enough of it because of our over-refined and highly processed diets. Our grandmothers used to call fibre roughage, and it is actually the fibrous portion of food that is not digested.

It is a beauty bonus because it contains absolutely no calories, so when you eat food with a high-fibre content you will not gain weight. The stomach and small intestine must work harder to separate digestible food from indigestible dietary fibre so this ensures an even flow of calories which stops you from feeling hungry.

It has been proven that fast elimination provides protection against bowel and colon cancer, the reason being that the shorter time that waste material is in the larger intestine, the less time for the formation of potentially carcinogenic toxic substances.

Fibre is found in all raw vegetables, fruit and natural grains. Bran, coconuts, almonds, figs, peanuts, green peas and chick peas are all high-fibre foods.

GARLIC

There is an old English folk saying: 'Eat onions in March, and garlic in May, and the rest of the year your doctor can play'. I have always believed that many of the old methods are the best; after all civilisation hasn't always had the products and pills of modern-day medicine to keep us together health-wise.

Garlic is packed with Allican, a miracle sulphur compound that fights infections and cleanses toxins from the blood, and it has been known for centuries to be an antiseptic. It has anti-cancer properties, and studies have shown that garlic can neutralise most of the environmental poisons that enter our body from food, air and water. For example, it can protect our bodies from the damaging effects of heavy metal poisons, lead and mercury to which we are all subjected both in the air, and in much of the food we eat.

Of course the major problem of garlic is that it is considered extremely antisocial to eat it raw, which is the way it should be eaten and the most palatable. However if it is cooked in soups and stews it usually will not make breath smell.

There are many different types of garlic pills on the health market which are mostly odourless. The ones I favour are especially formulated to protect against environmental toxins.

The Egyptians knew even 5,000 years ago that a clove of garlic was a magic potion. They called it 'The Great Panacea' and gave it to the workers building the pyramids to keep up their energy and ward off contagious diseases. It is known throughout the world that the antiseptic action of garlic combats viruses and bacteria and is particularly good in treating colds, flu, bronchitis and coughs. It also helps eliminate harmful bacteria in the stomach, and it can increase circulation, lower high blood pressure and unclog blocked arteries. All in all, you shouldn't be without a clove of garlic in your kitchen.

MY SECRETS

HOMOEOPATHY

Homoeopathic remedies have for centuries been touted as excellent cures for all manner of ailments. Rumour has it that certain long-lived members of our royal family swear by them.

My particular magic remedy for insipient colds and flu is called *oscillococcinum*. This comes in a course of tiny pills which, if taken scrupulously at the onset of influenza or a cold, can usually prevent it. They can be bought at most major chemists, and I swear by their effectiveness.

I always try to use homoeopathic remedies rather than patent medicines or antibiotics when I or one of my family is ill.

HONEY

Throughout the centuries, honey has been regarded as ambrosia, a divine food with age-retarding and life-prolonging properties.

At the risk of sounding like Barbara Cartland, I must extol the virtues of this delicious natural sweetener. Honey possesses miraculous nutritional and medicinal properties. In fact, many centenarians in Russia and Bulgaria eat an enormous amount of honey daily in their diet. A survey in Russia of 200 people who claimed to be over 100 years old discovered that many of them were actually beekeepers who, because they were also very poor, sold all their 'pure' honey and kept the 'dirty' residue to eat themselves. In fact, this residue was not dirty at all, and contained almost pure pollen-rich, unfiltered, unprocessed, natural honey, probably one of the healthiest life-enhancers that exists!

Honey is especially good for older people as it can increase calcium retention and help prevent nutritional anaemia. It is also beneficial for heart and liver disorders, colds, poor circulation, and complexion problems. Many books have been written about the magic of honey and I can only say that I agree with most of the things they have claimed.

Honey is neutral, moist, and can lubricate the intestines and the lungs, thus relieving sore throats, dry coughs and constipation. Singers have known for years about honey's healing properties, soothing their inflamed throats and tonsils. It is highly energising, yet at the same time soothing, particularly to people who are tired and over-stressed.

Honey has much more nourishment and natural sweetness than normal jams and marmalades, without the preservatives and colourings. And it is also a good sweetener in tea and coffee.

IRON

The most abundant trace mineral in the body, iron is the blood mineral necessary for the formulation of haemoglobin, the red pigment in blood cells which transports oxygen in the body. A large proportion of the population in Britain have an iron deficiency, especially women as a result of menstruating.

Since it is one of the minerals most frequently missing in the average person's diet, over five per cent of women receive less than the recommended daily allowance of iron from their food. The recommended

Life is a great bundle of little things.

(OLIVER WENDELL HOLMES)

daily dosage is 14.8 mg for adult females and 8.7 mg for adult males. It is difficult to get enough iron in your diet because it is found in animal organs like pigs' kidneys and lambs' liver (neither of which I particularly recommend) and curry powder. It is also found in wholemeal bread and dried apricots. The best way to increase iron in your diet is to take plenty of supplements, including vitamin C, and try to eat more foods that contain it.

JUICE

The benefits of vegetable and fruit juice have been known for centuries. What today's shopper doesn't seem to realise is that the benefits of packaged fruit juice that has been sitting on a supermarket shelf for six weeks are about equal to the benefits of a nice chewy Mars bar. The maximum vitamin and mineral content of juice can only be obtained if it is *100 per cent fresh*.

Orange juice should *always* be freshly squeezed and drunk within 10 minutes. Don't put it in the fridge, as it loses half of its nutritional content immediately.

Practically any vegetable or fruit can be juiced. One of the best, most nourishing and rejuvenating juices is that of the courgette. If that sounds revolting, it isn't! It is simply delicious, particularly if mixed with parsley juice, apple juice, or carrot juice. Go on a juice diet for a few days if you want to rejuvenate and refresh every single part of your body and feel a million dollars afterwards. Juice diets are often used to detoxify people with problems of the immune system because during juice fasting the body burns up and excretes enormous amounts of accumulated waste.

One of the world's foremost fasting authorities has proved that fasting on raw fruit and vegetable juices results in much faster recovery from disease, and effective rejuvenation of body tissue.

Juice fasting is far better and healthier than water fasting, which can be extremely dangerous without proper medical supervision.

JOJOBA OIL

This is one of the desert's ancient secret beauty treasures, a liquid gold that can help prevent and cure acne, get rid of dandruff and is a fantastic lubricant for the skin. Jojoba wax (oil) is pressed from the beans of the jojoba plant which grows in southern California, Mexico and Arizona. This oil has been used for centuries by the Indians for treating wounds, skin cancer, sores, and as a diet supplement.

Since jojoba oil is a close match to the skin's own natural oil, sebum, that is why it is an excellent oil to use for facial treatments, *particularly* if your skin is oily. Unlike most oils, it has a long shelf life and will remain fresh for some time after it is opened. Little is yet known about jojoba in this country, but I think it will be one of the most talked about beauty and health enhancers in the future. It can be used to moisturise, to put a sheen on your hair and even to make it grow. It can be used as a bath oil, a body conditioner, and it's inexpensive! Much cheaper than many of those myriad overpriced beauty products for sale in

An exceedingly rare shot of me in my kitchen. Beverly Hills, 1987.

department stores. You can buy jojoba at most health food stores.

KELP

Kelp is a form of seaweed, and some of its fibres have been found to clear radiation from the system. Before they started westernising their diet, the Japanese were among the healthiest, most vigorous and industrious race in the world. Their diet was largely vegetarian, with rice, some fish, but hardly any meat, and one of their staples was seaweed, or kelp.

Kelp is loaded with vital substances not available in most foods. It is extremely rich in natural iodine which is essential for the endocrine glands, especially the thyroid gland. Iodine deficiency can disrupt the normal functions of the thyroid glands, and thus cause diminished production of hormones. Since the thyroid hormone, thyroxine, is responsible for a youthful appearance, sex appeal, sexual vigour and libido, you can see that kelp is a pretty important thing to eat. It is also a natural source of selenium, which reduces cancers of the colon, stomach, liver and lung.

KISSING

Kissing, whether it's a baby, your grandmother or your lover, can be good for you. It puts a spring in your step, a sparkle in your eye and great expectations in your heart. Recommended daily!

LEMONS

Lemons are one of the best and oldest internal and external beauty treatments. Sailors away at sea for long periods used to be given a lemon to eat every few days to prevent scurvy, a result of vitamin C deficiency. The juice of a lemon contains more citric acid than any other citrus fruit, including the orange. Drinking a glass of diluted lemon juice with hot water first thing in the morning cleans and tones the digestive system. Hot lemon and honey before you go to bed at night is also the classic remedy for colds or flu.

Lemons also make an excellent inner cleanser, and purify the liver, tone the heart, help high blood pressure, poor circulation and varicose veins.

A great beauty treatment is to cut a lemon in half, squeeze it, and rub your elbows with the inside of the peel to soften and whiten them. The vitamin C helps the skin to make collagen – the protein that binds it together and maintains elasticity. Lemon juice, strained and mixed with warm water, gives hair a shining glow, and to make natural blond hair even lighter, squeeze lemon juice on it before sunbathing.

Here's my delicious and non-fattening recipe for lemon soufflé:

LEMON SOUFFLÉ

· S E R V E S 4 P E O P L E ·

3 large eggs
225g castor sugar
2½ lemons
300ml low-fat whipping cream if desired
1 × 15ml spoon gelatine
5 × 15ml spoons water
To finish: a little extra cream
2 × 15ml browned ground almonds

Prepare a 6″ or No. 2 soufflé case.

Separate the eggs. Place the yolks, sugar, grated lemon rind and heated, strained lemon juice in a basin and whisk over gentle heat until thick and mousse-like. Remove from the heat and continue whisking until the bowl has cooled. Put into a stainless steel saucepan. Half whip the cream and fold into the mixture.

Dissolve the gelatine in the water over a gentle heat and stir into the mixture.

Whisk the egg whites until stiff but not too dry; set the soufflé mixture on ice (the stainless steel pan allows the cold to penetrate the soufflé more easily) and fold in the egg whites. As the mixture begins to thicken, turn at once into the prepared case and put in a cool place to set. When firm, remove the paper, press the nuts or crumbs gently round the sides, and decorate the top with rosettes of cream.

LIPSTICK

Lipstick is the most glamorous cosmetic a woman can use. Not only does it give the face an instant lift but it also protects the lips from the elements, and can prevent little lines forming around the mouth. Lipsticks come in millions of different colours, textures and shapes. All women have at least one, because they know it is the quickest way to put a sparkle in your face, cosmetically speaking.

Lipstick was invented over 5000 years ago by the Egyptians in Babylon, and has been going strong ever since. It is my favourite cosmetic, and the one that gives the most benefit to the over-40 face.

MANGOES

Mangoes are, in my opinion, the most delicious of all fruits, even more delicious than papaya, and they are also extremely good for you. Scientists have found that they contain a natural anti-depressant chemical which has a soothing and calming action on the nervous system, help digestion, and are especially good for thin, over-active people.

A mango is also mildly diuretic and laxative. It calms the body, the mind and the emotions, whilst at the same time boosts energy. Mangoes have high fibre content and are very low in calories (approximately forty). If you cannot get your child to eat enough fruit, a mango will soon solve that problem.

NUTS

Nuts and grains are some of the most important and neglected of foods, densely packed with nourishment. Nutritionally they are unsurpassed by any others. They should be eaten raw, as they contain all the nutrients essential for human growth and can sustain perfect health and prevent disease and premature ageing.

They contain vitamin B1 and magnesium which are vital to the nervous system, and important minerals including potassium, zinc and iron. Chestnuts and almonds are the lowest in fat of all nuts, and peanuts are a good source of protein.

Nuts are extremely appetising, but they must always be eaten fresh, as once shelled they can go rancid quite fast which can be poisonous to the system.

MY SECRETS

OLIVE OIL

Although all kinds of oil are good for you, olive oil is probably the most beneficial. Many people have given oil a bad name in recent years, but it is essential to us, as long as we don't use saturated oil. We always need a certain amount of oil in our diet to keep our skin moist and our hair healthy.

People who live in Latin and Mediterranean countries have always known that olive oil is a wonderful food and medicine. It contains the most active alpha form of vitamin E, one of the best antioxidants, so you can use generous amounts of it for cooking and on salads, but may I stress, it must be fresh and *not* rancid. Greek and Cretan farmers often eat only hot fresh bread dunked in olive oil for their breakfast – how delicious!

Tests have shown that olive oil is the healthiest oil to eat, followed by sunflower oil and corn oil. It protects against cancer, arthritis and premature senility. For liver problems, take a spoonful of olive oil with a dash of lemon juice in the morning. Always use extra virgin olive oil when cooking and on salads because it is untainted by chemicals.

PAPAYA

Papaya, which has sometimes been called the 'Magic Melon' or the 'Youth Fruit', comes from Mexico. The Mexicans eat it as a dessert because, unlike most fruits, it helps the digestive tract to assimilate food more effectively if eaten after meals, and children absolutely love them.

It is an excellent cleansing food with therapeutic properties. Papaya and papaya juice are good for digestion, arthritis, and kidney disease. It is packed with vitamin C, and contains an enzyme called papain, which has been proven to dissolve the cross-linked proteins that accelerate the ageing process.

As they become riper, papaya, or 'paw-paw' as they are sometimes called, become yellow, fragrant, yielding to the touch and so delectable that you might want to eat more than one. However, a word of warning: papaya is supposed to have a calming effect on sexual desire! Some Far Eastern monasteries often give large amounts of 'paw paw' to the monks. So don't eat too much if you are in a happy loving relationship – it might be sexually inhibiting!

PASTA

Once spurned by dieters, there has been a rethink on pasta and it is now recognised as an excellent source of complex carbohydrates and one of the perfect energy foods. Choose wholewheat pasta as it contains fibre, and serve it with a light tomato and herb sauce, but do *not* be tempted into topping it with a rich, or cream sauce high in calories.

Here is one of my favourite recipes for pasta:

PASTA PRIMAVERA

· FOR 4 PEOPLE ·

500g penne
1 broccoli head
2 medium-sized courgettes
2 medium-sized onions
8 large mushrooms
2 large tomatoes
2 cloves of garlic
grated parmesan cheese (optional)

MY SECRETS

Cook the pasta in boiling water for 12 minutes (until *al dente*). Drain and refresh with boiling water (removing excess starch). Break the broccoli head into florets and cook in a steamer or colander over boiling water. Steam for seven minutes approximately (so that the broccoli is cooked, but still crunchy).

Chop the onions coarsely and sauté in a little butter until soft. (If you have a microwave no butter is needed. Put the onions in a bowl with about half an inch of water on the bottom. Cover with cling film and cook at a high temperature for two and a half minutes. When cooked, drain and add to the broccoli.)

Wash the courgettes and cut into 2″ strips. Cook in the steamer for about five minutes, or boil in water until cooked but not too soft.

Clean the mushrooms with a little salt and kitchen paper (or you can peel them). Place under a hot grill for a few minutes. Drain on kitchen paper. When cooked, cut into large chunks.

Concasse the tomatoes by placing them in boiling water for 10 seconds, then transferring them immediately to cold water. This allows you to remove the skin. Quarter, and cut each quarter in half again. Remove the seeds.

Crush the garlic and add to the vegetables. Season with salt and pepper. Add the vegetables (except the broccoli) to the pasta and reheat gently in a saucepan.

Place the broccoli back in the steamer for a minute to reheat and then carefully add to the hot pasta and vegetables. This prevents the broccoli from breaking up.

Add a little grated parmesan for more flavour but this is not essential. Serve warm – not too hot. It's scrumptious and another healthy dish that children will savour.

PERFUME

How gloomy the world would be without scent. The number of new fragrances that come on the market each year are mind-boggling. Some are wonderful and classic, and others are merely pale imitations, with a cheap, acidic aroma. Perfume is something that women should always use, and if you wear a signature scent, something that people will always remember you by, then you will always make an impression as you enter or leave a room.

I find the scent of bluebells so bewitching that I try to visit this bluebell wood near a friend's cottage every spring. Hampshire, 1992.

MY SECRETS

Put perfume wherever you want to be kissed. It's probably the oldest beauty enhancer that exists; we can read about perfume in ancient Egyptian manuscripts, Cleopatra never appeared without her perfumed oils and unguents.

I believe in changing my perfume as often as I change my shampoo because you become used to the scent – why should other people be the only ones to appreciate its fragrance?

QUICHE

One of my favourite meals, quiche is a classic of French cuisine. My preference is for spinach and mushroom quiche, and you can buy tasty ready-cooked ones everywhere. I don't usually approve of pre-packed foods but I will make an exception of this one!

Here is a delicious recipe for another quiche:

BACON, CHEESE & ONION QUICHE

PASTRY
175g plain flour
pinch of salt
90g butter or low fat margarine
30g lard
a little cold water to mix

FILLING
1 egg and 1 yolk
30g grated cheese
seasoning
145ml milk,
60g bacon
1 small onion or 12 spring onions
15g butter

Make the pastry by sifting flour and salt. Cut up fat and rub into the flour. Add cold water little by little and mix into a dough with your hands. Leave in fridge for twenty minutes before rolling out. Then line into a 7″ flan ring. Prepare the filling by beating the eggs in a basin, adding the cheese, seasoning and milk. Melt the butter in a small pan, add the bacon, diced, and then the onions, finely sliced. (If using spring onions leave them whole.) Cook slowly until golden in colour, then turn the contents of the pan into the egg mixture. Mix and pour into the pastry case. Bake at Reg. 5-6 until firm and golden brown (about 20-30 minutes). Serve hot or cold.

RAW

That's the way that you should try to eat most of your food. 65 to 70 per cent of your total diet should be raw. Obviously you are not going to eat raw meat – unless it's a fresh steak tartare – and eggs (I don't think you should eat much of these in any case), but *all* fruits, most vegetables, pulses and nuts are more nutritious when eaten raw. Many researchers now believe that the most potent and important foods of all are seeds, grains and nuts, mostly eaten uncooked. There have been many studies demonstrating how superior raw, living food is both for health maintenance and disease prevention.

Of course, if you live in a hot climate it's easier to eat raw foods, but naturally in the winter you need some cooked food like potatoes, beans, cereals, and bread. Not all vegetables are good eaten raw: rhubarb, asparagus and certain cabbages need to be cooked, but *not*, I stress, overcooked. Don't throw the baby out with the bath water – by which I mean if you boil your veggies

MY SECRETS

for too long all the goodness will be left in the water. You might as well eat a bag of crisps.

ROYAL JELLY

Royal Jelly is a delicious, powerful cocktail which I take a course of from time to time. It is known to increase resistance to disease and helps you to build up energy. It is particularly good for those are very active and play sports, or those who suffer from stress. Royal Jelly is the nutritive substance that the worker bees secrete and feed to the queen bee of the hive. 'Her magnificence' is much bigger than her subjects, and she lives 100 times longer than they do. Since she is the only bee in the hive capable of reproduction, it stands to reason that all the elements, vitamins and minerals necessary to life are in this extraordinary, potent food supplement which is given to her.

The best Royal Jelly I have found is the Api Regis brand made by Ortis. A 10-day course is recommended which you could take every six weeks or so, depending on how stressed or tired you are.

SESAME SEEDS

Sesame seeds have been used by man longer than any other seed. A staple food in India and China, they have been used by the women of ancient Babylon to make halvah (which is made with pounded sesame seeds and honey), a food they believed would enhance their sexual allure and restore their men's virility. The seeds were also valued by the Romans whose soldiers received an energy ration of cakes made with sesame seeds and honey which made them

work and fight harder, walk further and survive longer than on any other food of equal weight.

The sesame, which is called the King of Seeds, is richer in calcium than milk or nuts, and its protein content is almost 25 per cent higher than meat. But this is good, healthy protein, which also contains a high amount of lecithin. As well as proteins and minerals, sesame seeds are an excellent source of polyunsaturated fatty acids and the antioxidant, vitamin E.

Sesame and sunflower seeds are among the ten foods that are supposed to have a particular effect in maintaining and enhancing sexual vigour and longevity.

You should eat only raw, unroasted, hulled sesame seeds.

SUNFLOWER SEEDS

Sunflower seeds are concentrated nourishment, and the perfect snack food. They contain B complex and protein and are rich in polyunsaturated oils and vitamins B, E, iron and zinc. They are a very good antidote for fatigue, stress, depression and lack of energy. They are extremely nutritious and children love them, as do I.

TREATS !

However stringent a diet you are on, however much you are depriving yourself, exercising, saving your money, paying off the mortgage, or just getting through the week, you have *got* to give yourself a little treat now and then. By treats I mean anything you really enjoy – that chocolate bar here, that glass of wine there, or going to movies or for walks

with someone you care for. My biggest treat is travelling, which I indulge in as often as possible.

It's important to treat yourself well, because if *you* don't, who will?

Here are some of my favourite and most luxurious treats:

1. A cold shower on a hot day.
2. A hot bubble bath on a cold day.
3. Shopping – anytime, anywhere, unessential shopping is bliss! Whether it's clothes, candles, antiques or bric-a-brac, from upmarket department stores or out of the way boutiques or flea markets – I love to shop. Shopping boosts your adrenalin and quickly sends any worries and anxieties to the back of your mind – until the bills arrive! 'When the going gets tough the tough go shopping.' (This little slogan, embroidered on a pillow, was given to me recently.)
4. Freshly washed and ironed sheets (preferably sea island cotton, Porthault or Frette) with lots of contrasting or matching small pillows.
5. Come fly with me. I love to travel. British Airways is best, closely followed by Swissair and Lufthansa. Long-distance first-class travel is the most wonderful way to be pampered, and I usually arrive refreshed and feeling great.
6. A professional massage, facial,

No, this is not my own bed, but a set for a magazine shoot. It illustrates, however, how important the comfort of a bedroom should be – pillows, plants, peaceful music and privacy.

pedicure, manicure, all done in my own bedroom while watching one of my favourite videos.
7. Losing half a stone.
8. A frozen Mars bar when I've just lost half a stone!
9. Speeding across the sea in a powerboat on a beautiful, sunny, calm day on the Riviera.
10. Going to Paris – not just in April but any time.
11. Being given a present I've always wanted.
12. The scent of white lilies just after they've opened.

UNSATURATED FATTY ACIDS

Doctors are continually battling to get patients with cardiovascular diseases and high cholesterol levels to eat *unsaturated* fatty acids in cooking, and wherever possible.

Olive oil, corn oil, vegetable oils and oils derived from nuts and seeds should all be used instead of butter, coconut oil, and any oil that is solid at room temperature or is of animal origin.

It has been proven without a doubt that women in Japan, whose diet is *low* in saturated fats have far less incidence of breast cancer than women in the US and UK who eat a great deal of food with saturated fat.

VASELINE

This inexpensive and all-purpose emollient is probably one of the best things you can use for moisturising the skin of face and body, and toning and smoothing.

All the things you want a body cream or moisturiser to do for your body, Vaseline does just as well.

MY SECRETS

Although it's old fashioned and not particularly romantic because of its slightly antiseptic smell, it is one of the best emollients for keeping your skin, on both face and body, moist and supple and it's very inexpensive. (If you do put it on your hands at night, I suggest wearing cotton gloves to protect the sheets!)

An assistant I worked with on *Dynasty* had Vaselined her body every single night since she was ten. She had, without a doubt, the softest, most blemish-free skin on her body I've ever seen. I'd hate to think what her sheets looked like though!

WATER

Water is second only to oxygen as life's essential force and keeps everything – joints, cartilage, skin and mucous membranes – moist. It helps flush toxins out of the body, and moisturises it both inside and out. It is a natural diuretic because it helps in the secretion of excess sodium.

Because our bodies are sixty-two per cent water, we should drink seven glasses a day to balance our system. We drink more in hot weather, because we eliminate so much liquid through sweat and it must be replaced. Our body temperature is regulated through the cooling mechanism of sweat. We can live without food for ages, but we *cannot* live without water.

Dehydration, of which we are often unaware, comes from lack of water. You *cannot* rehydrate yourself with coffee, colas or milk; water is the only thing that will do it, but in actual fact very few people will actually drink a refreshing glass of water to quench their thirst. They prefer orange squash, coke or beer and consequently become even thirstier.

Alcohol, coffee, sugar and fat all remove water from our cells, and since we have lost approximately twelve per cent of the water that surrounds our cells by the time we are sixty-five, this needs to be replenished.

All fruits have a high percentage of water as do vegetables, particularly dark green vegetables like broccoli.

You don't have to buy bottled water – you can buy an excellent, simple machine, which filters tap water through a charcoal filter into a glass container, thereby removing most of the chemicals.

WINE

There is an Italian proverb that says 'A meal without wine is like a day without sunshine'. I fully agree. Doctors have recently changed their minds about the bad effects of wine on the metabolism, and now agree that half a litre of wine a day can actually *improve* your circulation, your heart and your well-being. It relaxes the blood vessels and it can also raise healthy fats in the blood. Red wine is actually better for your cholesterol than white. The nutritional and therapeutic values of drinking good wine (and good does not *always* have to be expensive) have now been accepted by many.

A glass of the grape is a great tension remover, and all foods taste better accompanied by it.

Most people think wine is fattening, but in actual fact one glass contains fewer calories (less than 75)

than a serving of rice, potatoes, or white bread. But you should not drink more than half a litre a day, which, divided into lunch and dinner, gives you approximately a couple of glasses at each meal.

Because wine contains tannin, which has an invigorating psychological effect, it can react like a tonic on the body, and red wine, particularly claret if it is an older vintage, is known to help recuperation after an illness.

YOGHURT

Live yoghurt contains *Lactobacillus Bulgaricus* which restores equilibrium in the stomach. Many health problems start when the natural balance between the good and bad bacteria is upset which can lead to constipation, gas and many more severe health problems.

The lactic acids in yoghurt act on the digestion in many ways, and have bactericidal properties that can stop a budding infection in its tracks. They synthesise the B vitamin group and increase the uptake of nutrients, particularly calcium, which yoghurt supplies in abundance.

One of the essential times to eat yoghurt, is after you have been prescribed antibiotics because although the antibiotics wipe out the bad bacteria they also wipe out the good. Doctors will seldom tell you this, but I consider it *essential* for anyone taking antibiotics to eat several cartons of live yoghurt a day to balance the bacteria level in their system.

People who cannot digest ordinary milk can get the same nutrients from yoghurt in a more easily digestible way.

I particularly like this recipe for the Greek tsatziki which is also a good diet food.

TSATZIKI
· F O R 4 P E O P L E ·
1 cucumber
30ml low fat yoghurt
1 clove crushed garlic
Tiny pinch of sea salt to taste

Peel the cucumber and cut in half, lengthways. Cut each half into three, lengthways. Remove seeds. Dice each strip into quarter-inch pieces.

Add the low-fat yoghurt and crushed garlic. If you must, add sea salt to taste just before serving. Do not add the salt too soon as it draws liquid from the cucumber and makes the whole thing too runny.

ZINC

Zinc is the second most important trace mineral (the first is iron) and has recently become a focal point in nutritional and medical circles. It promotes healing and growth and plays a key role in helping us maintain a healthy immune system, which these days everybody is trying to achieve. If the body is not given enough zinc, the protective T-cells will not form and the white blood cell count could become dangerously low, leaving the body vulnerable to any number of infections. Zinc deficiency is common among people who often catch colds and flu. Since the body cannot store zinc, it should be taken each day to ensure good health and continued rejuvenation. White spots on nails could be construed as zinc deficiency as twenty per cent of our zinc is stored in the skin.

Zinc is essential for the growth and development of the sex organs, and men need to take it after they reach fifty to keep their prostate gland healthy. It is known as an age retardant mineral and healing promoter.

The best food sources of zinc are: oysters, pumpkins, squash, fish, eggs, yoghurt, low-fat milk, wheat, bran, nuts, onions, sesame and sunflower seeds, sprouts and broccoli. However, the best way to see that you get enough zinc is to take one 15mg-25mg tablet daily.

BAD THINGS

ALCOHOL

Although half a litre or a couple of glasses of wine a day can be beneficial, alcohol in excess, and spirits in particular, are terrible for your skin and your liver.

Alcohol is a unhealthy diuretic which flushes essential minerals out of the body. It intensifies negative feelings such as depression and anxiety, causes insomnia, and sometimes nightmares. It also overloads the digestive system and is known to contribute towards heart disease and diabetes, causes stress, induces fat, and depletes our vitamins C and B and our stores of calcium, zinc and potassium.

People who drink a lot of alcohol should stock up on their B vitamins as alcohol depletes the body's supply, a consequence of which can be a deficiency in the lower part of the body, plus muscle cramps, weakness, numbness and tingling.

Excess alcohol consumption can also cause gout, brain damage and heart disease and raise your triglyceride (blood fat) level. It encourages thread veins to appear on the cheeks and 'grog blossoms' on the nose which are almost impossible to eradicate. Drunk in excess it can cause cirrhosis of the liver, which is usually fatal. Alcohol has practically no nutritional value and, contrary to what many people think, it is extremely addictive. It destroys brain cells at an alarming rate. If you look at fifty or sixty-year-olds who have been heavy drinkers all their lives, the ravages of alcohol are evident in their slurred speech, slow reflexes and thought processes, and bloated, veined and marked skin.

BUTTER

Although children grow up loving butter, there is now no question that a diet high in saturated fat contributes to heart disease and circulatory problems. Because fat builds up and is deposited along artery walls, it is very bad for blood circulation and leads to all manner of horrors: high blood pressure, heart attacks, cancer, hypertension and strokes. Butter is one of the fats that contain not only the most cholesterol, but also the most animal fat. It should be avoided as much as possible and a butter substitute used in its place.

BOREDOM

My mother used to say to me when I whinged as a child about having nothing to do: 'People who are bored

are boring.' That is as true today as it was then. How dare we be bored in a life that has so much to offer? We are spoiled today. We have countless television programmes, millions of books, magazines and newspapers, endless movies, plays and concerts to go to. With so many things to see and to do, it is a sin to be bored.

CAFFEINE

Caffeine raises blood pressure, speeds up breathing, increases stress, constricts blood vessels, raises stomach acidity, and alters the brain's normal natural chemistry. All those things should be enough to stop us drinking even one cup of tea or coffee a day but I believe that moderation, as always, is the name of the game.

Some recent studies have shown that even so-called normal levels of caffeine consumption, two to five cups of coffee per day, can affect the heart, and anything more than that can double the risk of heart attack. Consequently, if you must drink coffee (and I am one of those who must) try to keep it to under three cups a day.

Some people believe that drinking decaffeinated coffee is better for you, but the residue of chemical solvents used to remove the caffeine from the coffee beans can be more harmful than the real thing. Caffeine is also present to some degree in tea and all cola drinks.

CHOLESTEROL

In the past few years people have become obsessed with their cholesterol level. In the USA it has almost reached paranoia proportions with drugstores now selling tiny boxes of do-it-yourself cholesterol counters next to the home-pregnancy tests.

Cholesterol is actually an indispensable fat necessary for proper cell function, which ensures the fluidity and permeability of the cellular membranes. It is in excess, however, that it becomes extremely dangerous. It can cause heart attacks and many other cardiovascular problems, e.g. high blood pressure, angina and hardening of the arteries.

What most people do *not* realise is that there are two kinds of blood cholesterol – good and bad: LDL cholesterol (low density lipoprotein) is bad. HDL (high density) is good.

Human blood cholesterol has two origins: seventy per cent is synthesised by the liver, which means the body makes it, and only thirty per cent comes from food. That means you could live on lettuce leaves and mint tea and still have too high a cholesterol level.

Therefore to prevent your cholesterol levels from getting higher, it is extremely important to cut down on saturated fat. Meat, poultry, butter, dairy products, cheese and milk are particularly bad. Eating chicken without the skin cuts the fat content considerably.

To increase good cholesterol, one of the best things by far is olive oil which cuts down on LDL. Also beneficial are polyunsaturated vegetable fatty acids found in corn oil, sunflower oil, grape seed oil, and wheatgerm.

CIGARETTES

We know now that every single cigarette you smoke does you harm. Another nail in the coffin. Need I say more. Have you ever looked closely at the face of a person who smokes a lot? Look particularly around their lips. The tiny (and sometimes not so tiny) lines that spread out from their mouth like the face of some deranged clock are the result of inhaling fag smoke day after day. Ah yes, but *you* smoke I can hear you say. True. I have smoked since I was sixteen, but I have cut my consumption down to practically nil. As I have said before, I don't believe in depriving myself, and since some doctors believe that if you smoke *under* five cigarettes a day it does you less harm than being a passive smoker in a room or restaurant of people who are all puffing away, I choose to believe this. However, whenever I want a cigarette I think twice before I light it up, and often choose not to.

Recent reports have claimed that male smokers may be harming any children or grandchildren they might have, causing genetic defects and possible early death. These reports contained alarming statistics: 15,000 children, born between 1959 and 1966, whose fathers smoked more than twenty cigarettes a day, were *twice* as likely to suffer heart disease than those of non-smokers. A second study that analysed 220 children under fourteen with cancer, found that leukaemia, and cancer of the lymph nodes were *twice* as common in those whose fathers smoked in the year before they were born. Male smokers also face damaging their sperm count. *That* should make them cut down a bit!

Most of the harm is caused by oxidising compounds in the smoke, damaging DNA because the body can't keep up with the constant oxidation.

Several years ago I met a famous Swiss cancer specialist. When I reluctantly confessed to him that I smoked, he told me that if I could keep my smoking to five cigarettes or fewer a day, it would be highly unlikely that I would suffer from a smoking-related disease. This was good news indeed to one who likes to light up now and again. Since I have a great deal of willpower I heeded his advice and cut down radically. But if you occasionally see a photograph of me smoking a cigarette, please realise that it is only one of the two or three a day which I allow myself.

DIET DRINKS

I have never seen a thin person drinking a diet coke. All diet drinks contain a very high quantity of additives, synthetic fruit and plant extracts, caffeine and colourings. I would rather drink a glass of wine or water than a diet soda, particularly one that comes in a can. Recent research has even proved that drinking or eating *anything* out of a can can be toxic, as the lead and tin particles in the container can contaminate the substance and consequently, our bodies. Diet drinks also contain artificial gas which can cause stomach pains and gastritis.

DRUGS

What can one say about the most insidious, the most disgusting, the most hurtful, horrific substances known to mankind? Let's just say that *nobody* can be vital, energetic, healthy or beautiful if they take *any* drugs. If you know anybody who

MY SECRETS

does, and unfortunately many of us do, you would be doing them an enormous favour if you tried to get them to see the error of their ways and how they are shortening their lives.

Even over-the-counter, patented drugs can be harmful. Fifty years ago, doctors and pharmacists were still using the same natural, herbal, homoeopathic recipes and cures that had been used for hundreds, even thousands of years; now anybody who uses a natural form of healing is considered to be a bit of a crank. Over-the-counter pharmaceuticals are the norm, but I, and some doctors, believe that unless we really *need* to take prescription drugs, they can be damaging to the system.

The average person takes far too many drugs. Today, antibiotics are prescribed for even mild infections. The deadly thing about antibiotics prescribed over a period of years for minor strep throat or flu symptoms, is that if you become seriously ill or have an accident, and are in need of antibiotics, your body's immunity to them will have built up and sometimes they will not work. It is essential that you finish a course of antibiotics even if you feel better before the end.

Crack, cocaine, heroin, LSD, and new illegal drugs which are being invented all the time are the horror of our modern society. A drug addict has no considerate feelings for anyone or anything – all that matters is the next fix. It is the most tragic addiction of all, and terribly hard to cure, so if you're even contemplating an experiment with *any* kind of drug, DON'T.

I've seen too many friends, and too many careers ruined by drugs. I worked with a famous actor once whose energy was flagging during a scene. After four or five takes, he excused himself to go to his dressing room. When he returned I noticed a small 'moustache' of white powder which I realised instantly was *not* Max Factor's brand. 'Just a little boost, m'dear,' he smiled, suddenly filled with energy and bounce. We finished the scene, but I was uneasy about his forced vitality and counterfeit charm which was totally drug-induced.

I didn't see that actor again for several years, and when I did, the change was horrific. From being good-looking, virile, talented – one of the best actors of his generation – now at fifty-five, he looked like an old man. Skinny, almost bald, with white, papery skin, he was saggy-jowled and decrepit. Drugs had done a thorough job of ruining his career.

ENVY

Anger, envy, resentment and bitterness are all huge energy zappers. Jealousy being one of the worst. As a teenager at RADA I had a relationship which made me extremely jealous. As it turned out, I had good reason to be. The boy involved was a bit of a lothario to say the least. If I had been older and more experienced, I would have dumped him shortly after the relationship began, but as a young naive girl I hung on, suffering dreadful pangs of well-founded jealousy. It wasn't worth it; I learned never to get involved with that sort of relationship again, but how I suffered!

MY SECRETS

We learn all our lessons in life from experience. Life is the best teacher that there is and I soon learned that jealousy is extremely energy-consuming and draining. During this teenage relationship I was constantly exhausted, never able to do anything other than worry and fret. I also ate a lot, drank too much, and smoked like a chimney – all things which deplete your energy tremendously. Sometimes I couldn't even get out of bed in the morning I had been so fraught with jealous pangs. I know I was foolish, but who isn't in their teens? Most teenagers and twenty-year-olds have pretty low self-esteem, it is only as we get older that we become intelligent enough to realise how much better a person we are than we thought we were. So jealousy is yet another useless emotion we should rid ourselves of.

Envy cannot be controlled. I know enormously successful women who are eaten up by their envy of other women – many of whom are not even as successful as they are. If you find yourself envious of others, try to count all the positive things in your own life and imagine how many people might envy you. Think of homeless people, older, fatter, thinner, shorter, taller people – just don't think about being envious.

There will *always* be people better than you, and lesser than you. Banish envy from your mind.

FREE RADICALS

We've heard a lot about free radicals recently which are one of the most serious causes of degenerative disease of the human body, and possibly even the *main cause* of skin ageing. They are believed to contribute to major diseases, including cancer and heart disease.

So what are these terrifying little horrors called free radicals? They are molecules with an extra electron which makes them highly reactive and capable of causing bodily damage, especially to DNA coding, cellular structures, key cell enzymes and the immune system. Although a certain amount of free radical activity is needed to fight infection, an excess can trigger inflammation, damage lung cells and blood vessels.

Free radicals are formed from ultraviolet radiation from sun, airborne chemical pollutants, cigarette smoke, and other environmental agents of our dangerous modern age. Unless you inhibit the formation of free radicals by eating antioxidants in your diet, or taking supplements, they may accelerate the ageing process.

According to research, the nutrients beta carotene and vitamin E are the most effective natural antioxidants and free radical de-activators. They actually prevent the build-up of free radicals in the body. Although these antioxidants are not likely to repair damaged cells, they do seem able to slow down the ageing process and prevent some forms of disease.

GASTROENTERITIS

This is a condition that physicians are seeing more frequently these days, mainly due to improper handling of food in restaurants and homes and faulty methods of cooking frozen or packaged goods.

Gastroenteritis can be extremely unpleasant, with the stomach and intestines becoming inflamed due to the food poisoning. Then nausea, vomiting, diarrhoea, tummy cramps, and fever occur, and often severe dehydration and kidney failure, which in old people and young children can be fatal.

The best way to avoid getting this nasty infection is to make absolutely certain that instructions are obeyed *to the letter* in preparing all frozen foods – particularly when you are using a microwave. Hands, work surfaces and kitchen utensils must be scrupulously clean as well. It is also not considered advisable to eat any foods that are cooked on stalls in the street. Also beware of fast-food hamburger joints which have been known to cause outbreaks of gastroenteritis, not to mention the odd mouse tail mixed up in the mince!

HAMBURGERS

I'm sorry, I know that hamburgers are the national food of the USA and popular elsewhere, but I believe that eaten to excess, they can be terribly bad for you. The main reason is that the meat contains so many flavourings, colourings and additives, plus the dreaded saturated fat. This type of fat is the most damaging to our health and has been clearly linked to cancer and heart disease.

There have been too many incidences, often reported in the press, of foreign substances being found in ground hamburger meat, and parts of the animal which are *definitely* not considered edible. I know I don't want any of *that* in my stomach.

IRRITABLE BOWEL SYNDROME

Research into stress has borne out the theory that IBS is often caused by emotional stress, overwork, or not taking enough time each day for proper elimination. Our low-fibre diet is also a contributing factor to IBS, which many people do not even admit that they have.

The most common symptoms are: abdominal cramps, erratic frequency of bowel movements, which varies between constipation and diarrhoea, nausea, bloating, belching and flatulence. All of these can result in weakness, depression and chronic fatigue, not to mention embarrassment!

Having checked with your doctor to discover if any of these symptoms are caused by other more serious problems, an attempt to correct the condition should be made. Foods to be avoided at this time (although normally extremely beneficial) are carrots, Brussels sprouts, celery, garlic, cabbage, onions, baked potatoes, nuts and seeds, cauliflower, beans and lentils, and all dairy products except non-fat yoghurt.

What is left? Quite a lot actually: you can eat fish, poultry and veal, brown rice and as many fresh vegetables and fruits (with the above exceptions) as you wish. In addition, you should take three tablespoons of wheat or oat bran daily, and three to six ounces of unprocessed bran cereal to put the fibre content back into your body. One cup of hot water with one tablespoon of black molasses or maple syrup also helps.

You will have to experiment on yourself as to what does or doesn't cause IBS to recur. You will also have to be *extra* careful about alcohol, caffeine, and sugar substitutes. Eat slowly, chew longer, and take regular exercise.

JUNK FOOD

Eat junk, be junk! By its very name, junk food indicates the self-worth of the person who is trying to live on it. Doctors have recently discovered that children who live on a diet of junk food run the risk of developing scurvy, a disease which was supposedly wiped out in the last century. Junk food of hamburgers, hot dogs, buns, cakes, crisps and colas are unfortunately all things that young people seem to crave. Junk food is extremely dangerous as it pretends to be real food but is almost devoid of nutritional value. It is also the prime source of saturated fats, excess sodium, refined sugars, and refined carbohydrates. Avoid it!!

LARD

This greasy, fatty, sebacious, oleaginous, oily substance should be banned from your diet. It is one of the deadliest of the saturated animal fats and although it was extremely popular with our parents' generation, when the bread 'n' dripping sandwich was the hamburger of the day, I am glad to see that its popularity has waned.

If, however, you see your mother still pouring the bacon drippings from the frying pan into a jar, to refry again and again – stop her. It may be an oldie, but in this case it's definitely *NOT* a goodie!

LAZINESS

Laziness begets more laziness. I have often found that the lazier some people are, the more exhausted they become in doing the slightest thing that needs effort whereas often the people who do the most and achieve the most have the most energy. Lolling around doing nothing all day saps your energy. So get up and go! Go!! Go!!!

MEAT

Meat is something that I don't believe we should eat more than once or twice a week. Most meat sold today is filled with tenderisers, residues from the animals' feeding, pesticides and many other nasty substances. Added to that is the fact that meat from the EC's deep-frozen 'meat mountain' sold to British food processing firms, has recently been proved to be more than six years old! Do you want to eat *that* in your pies and sausages?

Meat and all animal proteins can cause acidity in the system, so the body loses calcium and actually excretes it in the urine. In addition, cooked meat forms chemicals which can be carcinogenic. Your body doesn't need high amounts of animal protein and fat – they impose a strain on your energy resources.

Here's a jolly statistic: a half-pound steak contains approximately 400 calories, plus twenty grams of fat (more than half of it saturated) and 130mg cholesterol. That's *before* you get to the french fries and the bread.

But whatever the pros and cons of meat, it's most men's favourite food,

so if you *must* serve it to your partner, try to make sure it's as lean as possible, and whenever you can, serve lamb, turkey, veal or chicken, rather than beef.

People of the Bantu Tribe in Central Africa eat no meat, and the women eat *no* animal protein at all. They have no signs of osteoporosis, even at eighty; that should tell you something.

NEGATIVITY

Negative thinking drags us down emotionally, physically and mentally. It's important not to allow negative thoughts to influence your mind, particularly if you, or one of your family has a life-threatening illness of any kind, as negativity can often exacerbate it. I believe that our thoughts are turned into active responses in our bodies. Many doctors today believe that cancer is caused by the onset of an emotional and stressful problem that triggers the disease.

I *know* from my own experience the power of positive thinking and how it can affect the environment that surrounds us, and the well-being of loved ones. When one of my children was seriously ill after a road accident twelve years ago, I sat by her bedside for six weeks and would actively not allow *anyone* to express *any* negative thoughts, opinions and feelings in her presence. Even though she was unconscious, I believed that those negative impulses would transfer themselves to her mind and prevent her from getting better. I was right – she recovered and is now perfectly well.

There is a story that illustrates the way negative and positive people react. Two little boys the same age are put into separate rooms. In one room there are wonderful games, toys and stuffed animals; in the other there is nothing except horse manure. When the two boys come out of their rooms they are asked what they had found. The boy with the toys says, 'Oh, it was rather boring, there was no-one to play with.' The other boy, all smiles, says, 'With all that horse manure, there must be a pony in there somewhere!'

OXIDATION

You can see what happens when rusty old iron cars in the knackers' yard oxidise. Just imagine that this horrible process is going on in our bodies *all* the time!

Normal oxidisation is accelerated by environmental oxidants coming from outside sources: cigarette smoke, pesticides and radioactivity are some of the worst offenders. But ageing, unfortunately, is also a cause of this corrosive process. There are no foolproof safeguards to oxidation, but antioxidant vitamins, as I have already said, are very beneficial and can halt this gradual disintegration.

PEPPER

I don't know why in all restaurants nowadays the waiter comes round at every single course, except the dessert, with a huge pepper mill. Pepper is one of the most irritating things that you can put in your body. It affects the stomach and the lining of the bowel and it is totally unnecessary. Black pepper contains small amounts of safrole, which is a known carcinogen, and greater quantities of the related compound, piperine.

PESTICIDES

So many of the fruit and vegetables we buy are sprayed with these noxious substances. There is little we can do to get away from them other than to wash them as thoroughly as possible. The average person consumes more than three pounds of pesticides a year. No wonder our bodies have to work so hard to eliminate all that poison.

QUACKS

There are a lot of bogus doctors and healers in the world, waiting to take your money and tell you all the things you want to hear. In the yellow pages you will see advertised 'miracle doctors', hypnotists, faith healers and all manner of practitioners who claim to cure all sorts of ills. Don't go to a doctor unless you know that he or she is a qualified member of the British Medical Association.

I have a friend who developed a serious back problem from having it manipulated by an unqualified practitioner. It amazes me that some members of the public are so gullible that they fall for a quack's promises. But, sadly, for some people these 'healers' are perhaps a last resort.

RANCID FOOD

Rancid nuts, meat, vegetables, dairy produce, or any food that's past its sell-by date are likely to make you ill.

Rancid nuts are among the most dangerous and toxic foods, but don't consume *anything* that looks or smells even slightly off. Even cereals and rice can go bad once they are opened.

Creams, lotions and cosmetics can go rancid as well. There is nothing beneficial at all in applying a skin product that is too old. Chuck it away. It can only do your face harm.

SALT

Too much salt can be toxic. We actually only *need* between 0.3 and one gram a day but the average person takes over seventeen grams, probably without realising it. So keep that salt shaker *out* of the way. Salt causes the body to retain water, and an excess can flood the system with as much as two to four extra quarts of fluid. This puts tremendous strain on the heart which then has to work twice as hard. Too much salt can also cause kidney damage, high blood pressure, heart and blood vessel diseases, cancer, and hair loss.

A certain amount of sodium is crucial to maintain the balance of fluid in our bodies, and it helps the heart, adrenal glands and kidneys to monitor our bodily functions.

Don't add salt to your food, since there is natural salt in every food that we eat, and watch those labels. All processed meats contain salt, as do canned foods, and even ice cream and biscuits. The World Health Organisation reported that an excess of salt in the diet can lead to cancer of the stomach; it is a proven carcinogen.

However, the good news on salt is that it is mainly the refined, commercial salt that is deadly. Sea salt (unrefined) or kelp are quite healthy if used sparingly.

SNACKS

One of the things I've always found

curious is that you rarely see a slim person or someone of average weight walking down the street eating a bag of chips or a sandwich. Snacking is one of the most fattening things you can do, and one of the most unhealthy. Our bodies, our metabolic processes and our digestion need a break between meals. If you must snack, do it just twice a day, between breakfast and lunch and between lunch and dinner.

It's true that our appetites usually sharpen up at those times, so if you need a snack try one of the dozens of healthy alternatives to chocolate bars and burgers: celery, carrots, fruit, health bars, hard candy or boiled sweets (filling but not particularly fattening), cottage cheese, or plain wholemeal biscuits with a little sugarless jam if you're desperate for something sweet.

TELEVISION

There is no doubt that watching too much TV can seriously damage your mental health. It has been proven today that by the age of twelve the average child has watched approximately 20,000 hours of television in their lifetime. (They have also witnessed several thousand murders and deaths on the box.) No wonder so many children today seem to lack moral values. When it is normal to see people shot, maimed, killed, attacked, raped and abused on TV, to some unformed young minds it might seem normal to do the same.

Values used to be learned from family, school and church, whereas today our children are taught much of their moral code from TV. Lack of respect for law and authority, and

endless violence – both make-believe and real – is too often depicted. Even though I myself have made an excellent living from TV, I think it is the most insidious destroyer of minds today.

TRIGLYCERIDES

The formation of excess triglycerides, which are fats in the blood (rather like cholesterol), can be directly linked to alcohol abuse and consumption of too much sugar, white bread, egg yolks, fatty red meat, corn, potatoes and soft drinks. Oral contraception can raise levels, and triglycerides cause heart attacks when the body has an excess.

ULTRAVIOLET RAYS

These rays, which emanate from the sun, are terribly damaging to the skin. To protect itself from ultraviolet rays, the skin produces a pigment called melanin, which is the substance that turns you brown in order to protect your skin. With the thinning of the ozone layer, there is now not enough atmospheric protection from these damaging rays. Doctors are treating more and more skin cancers and they believe it is because of the sun's ultraviolet rays. The best protection is to wear sunblock on your face and any exposed skin *all the time*, even in winter. Limit sun exposure, and if you *must* sunbathe, do it before 10.30 a.m. or after 4 p.m. I know it's not much fun, but neither is skin cancer.

VIOLENCE

Violence is an anathema in our society which sadly seems to be getting worse.

MY SECRETS

Don't tell me that violence is just the result of young, jobless, poor men letting off steam. I am *convinced* that the film industry is, in many ways, responsible for the horrific amount of joyriding deaths, random stabbings, killings and abuse against men and women today. Since the Government doesn't seem to want to do anything about it (talk is cheap), I think that it should be the responsibility of those who are running our networks, making our movies and putting our television shows on the air, to *stop* glorifying and glamorising death and violence.

Without sounding like an old-fashioned prude, I have to say that I think that censorship has now become necessary in certain cases. All this nonsense about self-expression and freedom of the individual and do your own thing only encourages those with the basest tastes to commit their often depraved fantasies to the screen and pervert the impressionable minds of our children and young adults.

One day I hope my children will have children of their own and although I may not be around to see my great-great grandchildren, I would like to think that the world is going to be a fit place for them to live and thrive in happily. For this, we must find a way to stop the violence in our society.

WHITE FLOUR, WHITE SUGAR (AND EVERYTHING MADE WITH THEM)

When I was a child, and there was no glue in the shops, we used to stick things in scrapbooks with a paste made from flour and water. White flour, and everything made with it, is really nothing more than white paste.

There are many lovely-looking pseudo foods made of sugar and flour but they are usually high in calories and completely lacking in nutrition. Of course we like them, and our children love them because they have nice flavours and look yummy, but it is too easy to get addicted to these products.

It has been proven that eating a diet high in white flour and sugar causes severe swings in mood from anxiety to deep depression. These foods also cause obesity, the risk of heart disease and damage to the immune system. Doctors, scientists and nutritionists have written endless books about the dangers of these carbohydrates, so I will save you time: just avoid refined carbohydrates. They are metabolised by the body which then dumps insulin, and although this may create an instant spurt of energy, it is usually followed by prolonged lethargy. This high-low swing puts an incredible strain on the body, especially the heart.

White sugar and flour do not satisfy our hunger but perpetuate it, that is why so many people who eat a lot of foods containing white sugar and flour – buns, cakes, biscuits, sandwiches, puddings and stodgy desserts – suffer from obesity, and are always snacking because they are hungry. White sugar has recently been linked to many kinds of cancer and stomach disorders. These refined foods should be cut out of your diet.

X - R A Y S

Excessive exposure to x-rays can be harmful. My advice is that unless it is absolutely necessary, do not let yourself be x-rayed, it can cause premature ageing and x-ray poisoning (which causes the hair to fall out). It increases the likelihood of genetic deterioration, and even when administered by a qualified medical practitioner, subjects the body to potentially deadly radiation.

Some ninety per cent of all x-rays done today are thought to be unnecessary, so unless you've broken some bones or are over forty-five, (when all women should have a bi-annual mammogram) don't have unnecessary x-rays, even on your teeth.

YELLOW TEETH

One of the first things that we notice about a person is their teeth. Strong, healthy teeth are a barometer of good health and beauty and certainly not difficult to achieve today.

The health and hygiene of teeth has improved 100 per cent in the past 150 years; having yellow teeth is both unattractive and unnecessary. The yellow often comes from excessive smoking or drinking tea or coffee. If nothing is done about it, the teeth will continue to darken. You often see old people with teeth so dark that they almost look black. This is due to the build-up of plaque which starts behind the teeth, but eventually spreads all over them. Most good dentists will remove plaque very easily and there are many excellent forms of toothpaste on the market today which help prevent it. If the condition has gone far it is best not to scrub your teeth so that you wear them out, but go to the dentist as soon as possible.

Teeth naturally lose their whiteness as they age. An excellent home remedy to whiten teeth is to brush them with sea salt every other day. Visit your dentist, as he or she will be able to bond or bleach to whiten your teeth.

ZITS

These nasty little spots, bumps and pimples – whether acne, eczema, hives or psoriasis – can ruin the life of adolescents, and older people too. They are created by too many toxins accumulating in the blood, probably due to a malfunction one of the organs of elimination in the body, liver, colon, kidneys or lung. This leads to the blood heating up which then affects the skin.

There is no knowing at what age zits strike. I myself went through a period in my thirties when I woke up one day and, to my horror, found my face covered in red spots! There are all kinds of reasons for this, and I suggest until they disappear, sometimes of their own accord, a general cleansing and also a good cosmetic cover-up is needed. Don't eat cheese, chocolate or coffee as these can exacerbate the problem.

Unfortunately zits, like the common cold, are hard to get rid of but here is one good cure which I have found helps. Put a slice of garlic, a dab of milk of magnesia or some nail polish remover on the spot before you go to bed. Press hard, and in the morning it should be much less visible.

MY SECRETS

Finally, here are my ten rules for remaining healthy, youthful and vital for *ever*:

1. You are as young as your mind. *Think* young – embrace new ideas and philosophies. Discard what doesn't work for you.

2. Exercise often.

3. Laugh a lot.

4. Eat as much uncooked, raw, living food as you can. Give your body the best possible fuel. Only eat when you're hungry.

5. Maintain your appearance. You should be proud of how you look. The way you show yourself to the world shows the world how you think of yourself.

6. Try to drink a litre and a half of water *between* meals every day. Never drink carbonated diet drinks or sodas.

7. Stop smoking. If you can't, cut down to under five a day.

8. Love someone or something. Even if it is just your dog or your job, love it a *lot*.

9. Have a glass of wine, a piece of chocolate, or a biscuit if you feel like it. It won't kill you, and constant deprivation is not what living well is all about.

10. Appreciate the beauty that still exists in this world around us.

MY SECRETS

Desiderata

GO PLACIDLY AMID the noise and the haste, and remember what peace there may be in silence. As far as possible, without surrender, be on good terms with all persons. Speak your truth quietly and clearly; listen to others, even to the dull and the ignorant; they too have their stories. Avoid loud and aggressive persons; they are vexatious to the spirit. If you compare yourself with others, you may become vain or bitter for always there will be greater and lesser persons than yourself. Enjoy your achievements as well as your plans. Keep interested in your own career, however humble; it is a real possession in the changing fortunes of time. Exercise caution in your business affairs, for the world is full of trickery. But let this not blind you to what virtue is; many persons strive for high ideals, and everywhere life is full of heroism. Be yourself. Especially do not feign affection. Neither be cynical about love; for in the face of all aridity and disenchantment it is as perennial as the grass. Take kindly to the council of the years, gracefully surrendering the things of youth. Nurture strength of spirit to shield you in sudden misfortune. But do not stress yourself with dark imaginings. Many fears are born of fatigue and loneliness. Beyond a wholesome discipline, be gentle with yourself. You are a child of the Universe no less than the trees and the stars; you have a right to be here. And whether or not it is clear to you, no doubt the Universe is unfolding as it should. Therefore be at peace with God, whatever you conceive Him to be. And whatever your labours and aspirations, in the noisy confusion of life, keep peace in your soul. With all its sham, drudgery and broken dreams, it is still a beautiful world. Be cheerful. Strive to be happy.

FOUND IN OLD ST PAUL'S CHURCH, BALTIMORE, DATED 1692

MY SECRETS

PICTURE CREDITS

2-3 Eddie Sanderson; 6 Eddie Sanderson; 8 Joan Collins; 10 Joan Collins; 12 Joan Collins; 14 Joan Collins; 15 Joan Collins; 16-17 Joan Collins; 23 Judy Bryer; 27 Eddie Sanderson; 30 Eddie Sanderson; 32 ABC; 35 Judy Bryer; 40 Mike Owen for *Marie Claire*; 43 Gilles Decamps; 46 Annie Leibovitz; 47 Eddie Sanderson; 48 courtesy of Paul Keylock; 49 Joan Collins; 50 Eddie Sanderson; 52 Joan Collins; 53 courtesy of Paul Keylock; 55 Joan Collins; 56 Steven Berkoff/Astrid Worth; 58 Eddie Sanderson; 63 Eddie Sanderson; 65 Eddie Sanderson; 66 Eddie Sanderson; 70 courtesy of Paul Keylock; 73 Eddie Sanderson; 75 Joan Collins; 80 Eddie Sanderson; 82 Judy Bryer; 84-95 Eddie Sanderson; 96 Eddie Sanderson; 98 Friedman-Abeles; 99 top picture – Roddy McDowall, bottom picture – Boyan Coren; 100 Joan Collins; 102-3 Astrid Worth; 109 Eddie Sanderson; 110 Eddie Sanderson; 111 Joan Collins; 112 News of the World; 114 George J Grimes; 116 Joan Collins; 118 James Douglas; 119 Ron Kass; 122 courtesy of Paul Keylock; 123 Gary Bernstein; 127 Gary Bernstein; 128 Joan Collins; 131 top picture – Joan Collins, bottom picture – Hulton-Deutch Collection; 132 Mike Owen for *Marie Claire*; 133 Joan Collins; 134 Joan Collins; 135 Eddie Sanderson; 136 top picture – Joan Collins, bottom picture – Peter C Borsari; 137 Joan Collins; 138 Joan Collins; 139 Joan Collins; 140 David Seymour/Magnum; 143 Mike Owen for *Marie Claire*; 144 Mike Owen for *Marie Claire*; 145 Mike Owen for *Marie Claire*; 146 Joan Collins; 147 Doug McKenzie; 148 top picture – Jean-Pierre, bottom picture – Joan Collins; 149 top picture – Joan Collins, bottom picture – Earl Miller; 150 Joan Collins; 153 Joan Collins; 155 courtesy of Paul Keylock; 156 Joan Collins; 157 Jean-Pierre; 158 Joan Collins; 161 Joan Collins; 166 Eddie Sanderson; 171 David Girvan; 173 Eddie Sanderson. Running head photographs courtesy of: Gary Bernstein; Joan Collins; Alan Davidson; John Swannell.

ACKNOWLEDGEMENTS

I would like to thank Gary Bernstein, Eddie Sanderson and Mike Owen for their invaluable photographic contribution to this book.

And Michael Alcock, David Inman, Sarah Mahaffy, Sarah Browne and Roger Hammond for their patience, enthusiasm and faith in me.

For more information, please contact:

Paul Keylock
The Joan Collins Fan Club
44 Celeborn Street
South Woodham Ferrers
Chelmsford
Essex
CM3 7AE